AMBIT

KU-300-642

is edited by
Martin Bax

with the assistance of
Kate Pemberton (*Assistant Editor*)
Victoria Howe (*Subscriptions Manager*)
Gwen MacKeith (*Editorial Assistant*)
Judy Bax (*Financial Director*)

Editors
Julia Casterton (*Poetry*)
Carol Ann Duffy (*Poetry*)
Mike Foreman (*Art*)
Henry Graham (*Poetry*)
Geoff Nicholson (*Fiction*)

Corresponding Editors
J.G. Ballard
Taner Baybars
Richard Dyer
Nichola Grey
Vanessa Jackson
Henry Lowther
E. A. Markham
Eduardo Paolozzi
Ron Sandford
Satyendra Srivastava
Irving Wardle
Eugene Wolstenholme

The magazine is designed by
John Morgan/Omnific and printed by
The Lavenham Press Ltd.

Ambit editorial address:
17 Priory Gardens, London N6 5QY, UK

Bookshop Distribution:
Central Books / tel. 020 8986 4854

See back flap for details of how to order
a single copy or take out a subscription.

Visit our website: ambitmagazine.co.uk

Issue 175, Spring 2004

ISSN 0002-6972

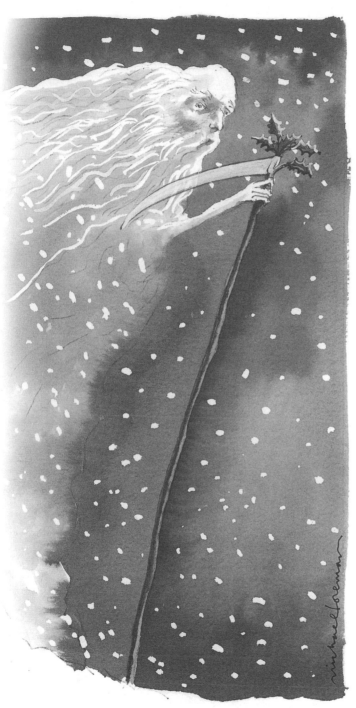

Judy Gahagan

Calling up the Gypsies

They're Back

The gypsies are back –
their skirt-swirling swiftness
twisting and turning past heaps of water-melons
through puddles, indifferent to the trucks,
the shifting trash of the outskirts
where exiles live

zigzagging between languages
unabashed, skirts tumultuous
dwelling nowhere, anywhere,
dwelling in the moment
of thrusting out their hands, palms up,
wailing their want-lament

faces that sheer ruthlessness
you can trust
to not apply, request or beg;
they demand, they thrust
their insistence;

they catch up
with my pale evasions
as I post a letter to you
demanding nothing
but between the lines
the want-lament that won't reach you

Out of the Dark

Because you came from out of the dark
uninhabited hours beyond the curfews
of my quotidian
                         because your call
came out of the dark unmarked hours
where exiles live

reached out across the abysmal
gulfs between us
                   because your voice
was slow, its inflections charismatic

the ikon I'd painted of you
your ecstatic look
the iconostasis of your remote country
the continuously falling snow of it
rose in my candlelight.

The candles reach and sway
ludicrous and ecstatic
as the gypsy diva
colossal in red satin
singing the *cantec de mehale*
the songs of the outskirts

pouring out her vibrato in a concrete shed
tremolos souped up
singing in falsetto the basics:
live passionately, live passionately

The Book of the Gypsies

In the book of the gypsies you left behind
in me when you left
was a photograph of an ancient
dark as her origins and darkness
filled the runnels of her crumbling face
her eyes too were bottomless

she seemed to be staring into the abyss
of her life's ending
but she was swathed in chiffon –
bridal white, flower-strewn
as if the songs of the lautari
had called up a perpetually flowering girl

or maybe she was decked out for death.
But her eyes burned out of the book
too passionate for a book, too passionate for death:
it's not too late, not too late.

Sitting Out

Uprooted these migrants
have dragged two tree stumps
from the remainders of the park
behind their lean-to café
to sit outside and smoke and talk
amidst the slowly moving trash
on the pavement by the bus stop
music pouring out around them

as once they must have sat by the village
by the fragrant teeming forest
wreathing smoke with talk across
the soon-to-be-abandoned valley
at this hour when the mountains' black
would enclose a heavenful of stars
music – hurtling gypsy music –
pouring out around them.
Uprooted they could show me
how to dwell.

King of the Gypsies

The house I choose for us
is the house the king of the gypsies built:
a palace of nine turrets
fine-fretted covered balconies to spy into the inner court;
six great salons
of textured, opalescent walls with murals of the legends
of your life;
no doors but for the heavy hanging skeins of beads
the tinkling veils
would keep our solitude intact in a shared house
the shimmer between us.
An uninhabitable house
without foundations, water, wiring, power, pipes.
Like the gypsies
that *'prophetic tribe with smouldering eyes'*
we'd live outside
in the midnight-coloured nights alive with fireflies.

Refugees

Scavengers have an intent blind look –
the look of the skinny fox
living on the scrub-land by the railway
flaunting the auburn of his tail

the look of the refugees
in campsite clothes clutching their mobiles
and their languages

the look of the gypsies doing the Grand Parade
trawling the shoppers, trawling the shops
in their tumultuous skirts

my look on hungering days
richly at home but starved of you
staring at my remaindered ikons

the look of the ones who live on the outskirts.

The Iron End

My heart's harvest falls
at the iron end of the year
on the cusp between the deaths of November
and the time when mauve veils
the thickening tree buds,
still iron, still winter,
the *negritude* of everywhere
challenging the light of spring.

My imagination follows you
where accumulating silence
never changes its progress nor its effects.
The gulf between us is unbridgeable
our intimacy intact.

Judy Gahagan has published poetry, prose and translations in a number of magazines; a volume of short stories, two pamphlets and two volumes of poetry. She runs courses in psychology and poetry and has recently completed a novel about dream research and a verse biography of Ludwig II of Bavaria.

Island / Neil Sproul

Keith is on the lookout for *signs*. Lying in the bath now he has made his fat belly into an island. This island is volcanic (his gaping navel its crater). And his belly the island is Keith himself – his bloated, refracted body beneath the bubble-bath spume is his hidden depths, only the island protruding for the world to crash waves at.

Keith is close to fucking nuts. So many therapists have hinted so – to Keith's pleased affirmation – but as yet none have given Keith his desired piece of information: he is an *artist* in all this. His making of nothing into something is his search for eternal truth. Beatified Keith is in a long line of suffering aesthetes, singing canaries in the mines of the human soul.

Instead he's told to leave it alone. One therapist (not fully accredited, it later turned out) likened Keith to a man with a temptingly juicy scab. He just can't stop picking it. Forget that guy. Strike one therapist.

Look at his belly. Keith is into the interconnectedness of all things. His belly is an island, is an affirmation of what Keith has essentially known before now, but has only these enervating past three days found to be true. It is also his dad's head. Keith's dad, who had this thing about being *exactly* six foot had a party trick way of proving it. *Watch* he'd tell Keith at the swimming pool, and Keith would watch as his father swum to the deep end (six feet deep), then let air out of his mouth until he was standing, soles flat, on the swimming pool floor. And he was indeed *exactly* six feet! The crown of his head met the troubled meniscus of the pool, just and no more.

A hairy man, matted when wet, Keith's dad was ironically bald on top. This he concealed by growing fronds on either side of his crown and gumming them cunningly with spit. But in the swimming pool these fronds were freed, and now the childhood Keith is witness to the top of his father's head lurking as a terrible octopus. When he surfaces to beam his triumph at his *exact* six feet, the octopus has its tentacles running over his face, close to success in its bid to hook into Keith's dad's mouth (minus dentures).

Now Keith's island belly is him exposed *and* his dad's head. Keith has grown to be a hairy freak himself and his belly exudes black thread, which in the ocean lapping the island waves and drifts.

It is interconnected, a sign: the belly, his self, his dad's octopus head. Keith nods and considers his recently discovered truth.

Keith had clued in this therapist from the start. This therapist has been told that Keith is a writer and his search for self expression is a burden he shoulders dutifully. (Even Keith doesn't go as far with this as he'd like: Calvary looming at the end of the street, his burden cutting into him, the crowd of therapists jeering, the morons.)

The therapist looks at her clock. There are ten minutes, she tells Keith, perhaps too brief a time to broach such an issue, but does Keith ever become confused as to who he actually is? Are there maybe some famous figures, contemporary or historical, writers perhaps, who Keith is unusually empathetic towards? Does Keith find he is up one day and down the next? Very very up? Deeply down?

Keith is striking another therapist from his life. He knows enough therapist babble to know where she is heading with this. Neither manic nor delusional, Keith is the real McCoy. There is silence until time's up. Coat on and he's out of there.

A cold night. Dark too. Keith thrusts his hands into his pockets, sinks his head deep into his coat's collar. His body language says pissed off, says wronged man, fuck off. He trudges up the hill to his house.

Keith lives in a small town. It is rare to go out and not see someone you know. People in small towns have mastered the small town greeting: raise eyebrows, a cheery *Hi!*, keep walking. Otherwise how would you make it down the street, the shopping to do and constantly waylaid by the Joneses, the Carruthers-Smythes?

This has just happened to Keith. Someone has passed him, done the small town thing, kept walking before Keith can remember who he is. He ponders this while walking, the man's face on the tip of Keith's tongue, so to speak.

By the green-man crossing he has it. An ex-therapist is all. Keith tuts. Crosses.

And then something odd happens. Another passer passes, says *Hi!* and he is an ex-therapist too!

Artist that he is, Keith is quick on the look out for signs. He is after portents that something significant is afoot. He *feels* it, but indicators that it is so? The street is as ever, its Indian restaurant, its punters illumined in the greenish glow. The sky too: sure the clouds could be said to be scudding a bit, concealing the crescent moon like a, like a *veil* – but this is pretty standard stuff.

Lacking a good enough sign Keith goes home and takes a bath. He hasn't yet noticed the stuff with his belly the island, his dad's head.

Next day and Keith is pursued by ex-therapists, hunted by them wherever he goes. They are coming in the fucking windows Keith thinks, and takes himself into the country for a walk where he will be safe.

The farmer mowing his meadow is an ex-therapist! He had once told Keith to tell himself that some things are just nothing, not significant, only nothing. He spots Keith rooted and staring. The farmer raises his eyebrows, says *Hi!*, but Keith has raised his fist, shaken it at the fucking moonlighting farmer and has high-tailed back down the road to town.

The library. Ex-therapists! The fish shop. Ex-therapists too! It is all Keith can do to fumble his keys from his pocket, let himself panting into his house, there to sit and ponder its meaning. It's a sign, definitely. But what? Keith dare not turn on the telly.

Day three and he's been up since before dawn planning it out. He has the curtains shut (spies no doubt, the ex-therapists) and he has campaigned logically on paper. What is happening is not run-of-the-mill stuff. That Keith must get to the bottom of it is plain. To do this he must interview his enemy, thrust himself deep into the nest of vipers.

But therapists will never front up with the truth! This is *transference* they have always told Keith when he has tried to ask them stuff about themselves in the past. Let's talk about you, Keith. This is why you're here, yes?

Bastards. Keith will need to be more cunning.

Keith in front of his bedroom mirror. Sunglasses, but not enough disguise to fool these ex-therapists. He thinks of the part of him that they must be most familiar with and lights on his hands. The ex-therapists have seemed to take an inordinate interest in what he's doing with them, biting their fingertips, cracking knuckles, drumming them on the back of the sofa. He fishes a pair of leather gloves from his chest of drawers and pulls them on.

Sunglasses, gloves – still not enough. The lower half of Keith's face is clearly recognisable. This he cannot cover. But with a scarf to retreat his chin into he can at least make his visage fleeting.

Keith in front of his bedroom mirror. Perfect. Let them recognise him now!

He has decided on the pub at the end of his street. Full of fucking ex-therapists! A rat-run of them! The one serving at the bar had been struck from Keith's life for suggesting the most ridiculous cognitive behaviour therapy imaginable. She had told Keith to stop at certain points of the day and ask himself: Come on Keith, what is the *worst* that could come of this?

Ludicrous! Such a relative judgement – the worst only being limited by one's imagination (and Keith's was an *artist's*) and by the fact that to believe in the inadmissibility of the *worst* relied on the fact that *worst* things didn't happen all the time. Worser. The world was the worst place.

That ex-therapist bar-maid was an arsehole and Keith believed in taking his enemy by the neck. The arsehole's neck.

'A pint of bitter,' said Keith.

'Pardon?'

Keith emerged his chin from his scarf, said it again. The bar-maid looked at him searchingly, the bitch, but nodded and agreed a pint of bitter he could have.

In fact, there were several searching looks directed at Keith from punters all round the pub. Ex-therapists of course, their eyes stumbled, were repulsed at the walls of Keith's sunglasses, his scarf and gloves. He couldn't help but grin – those ex-therapist fools! Analyse this!

His pint placed before him, Keith used its shelter to spread out his campaign plans on the bar. He had a set of questions to ask, get to the bottom of all this, find out what it means, what's being said to Keith.

Look at that bar-maid there – she's called the ex-therapist landlord from the backroom and now they are muttering to each other, trying not to let Keith see what they're up to. He pulls his scarf higher and says *Idiots!* out loud. He can't help but shake his shoulders in mirth. How that makes the ex-therapists stare, their muttering in Keith's direction redoubled!

First step of campaign: he will call for crisps and over the ex-therapist must come. Keith can barely contain himself – he has positioned himself so well, at the bar directly under the shelf where the crisps are kept, that as the ex-therapist stands on a stool and reaches up, Keith will have her in position for questioning.

Question one is a statement. 'I know who you are,' Keith says, pushes his sunglasses further up his nose.

The barmaid stiffens.

'I know who you are,' he tells her again.

He has her. She is thrown. Ignorantly, she sticks to her role. 'What kind of crisps do you want?'

Question Two: 'How long has this town been run by you people?'

She is genuinely alarmed now, her cover blown. 'I'm sorry,' she blusters, 'I don't think I can hear you right.'

'How long has this town been run by you people?'

'Maybe if you took your scarf off I might hear you better.'

Keith laughs bitterly. 'Yes, that's what you'd want.'

The bar-maid fucking ex-therapist is on the run and jumps down from the stool, four crisps bags in her hand. 'Look, just choose which one you want, o.k.?' She puts them in front of Keith and scampers to the other end of the bar, there to resume her muttering with her ex-therapist boss.

Time for step two of Keith's campaign. He feels analytical eyes bore in to him from all sides, but he is determined to go on. He drains his pint of bitter and signals to the bar-maid that he would like another. The landlord elbows her and over she comes.

This time Keith is having Guinness, long pouring, slow and bar-maid rooting. He says, 'Who controls you?' Louder, so she can't feign the muffling of his scarf, he shouts, 'WHO CONTROLS YOU?'

With a yelp the pathetically beaten ex-therapist bar-maid is off, seeking refuge behind the back of her boss.

Keith's question is answered. He sizes the landlord up.

The landlord stares back at Keith.

The other fucking ex-therapists in the pub have shut their traps.

Grinding a cigarette into an ashtray, the landlord prepares to speak. The smoke from the cigarette pools around him, sliced through with swords of sunlight. He is framed by the town's coat of arms on the wall behind him.

Keith knows the ex-therapist boss, the boss of the ex-therapists, has arranged all this for effect. Keith is not intimidated. But his blood is up – he shouts, 'YOU! You control them! Why are you following me? What is it all for?'

It is too much for the landlord. Suddenly his face is conciliatory. Body language: palms out, feet apart. Keith suddenly feels sick with loathing. 'Now mate,' the landlord says. 'We don't want any fuss in here.'

'Don't you *mate* me!'

'Look around you,' the vile ex-therapist is pleading. 'This is a family pub. A local pub.' He gestures around the room. 'We all know each other.' The punters nod in agreement, stare at Keith, at the scarf he pulls higher.

It is worse than Keith thought, but it is an affirmation. They are entwined like strangling roots. A net of them. He nods, cannot restrain a hoot of laughter. 'Oh you bastards,' he tells them. 'Talking, talking.' He rises to leave, at the door parts with, 'But I know. I'll get to the bottom of this! Analyse that, you chattering monkeys!'

Into the dead air following Keith's departure, the landlord says, 'We'll get some mileage out of him.'

The punters nod, grimly.

In the bath, Keith's belly is an island and the island he now understands is him. This is the sign he is sent: he is the only one left. Everything else is a sea of therapy beating at his shore. There is the symmetry of his dad's octopus head also. And thus it is so.

Neil Sproul lives in East Sussex. He has had work published in Cutting Teeth, Chapman and Orbis. He recently completed his first collection of short stories.

Julian Bell

Lyme Regis, 1956

Sea fills the window,
gentle and vast,
and all theirs.

They hold hands in two chairs,
half an arm's length apart,
saying nothing.
What is there to say?

Except that the tide
stirs and slaps,
turns on itself,
returns and leaves.

She wakes incredulous
on a foreign shore.
A saltwater stain marks where he's been,
a man's print, mingled with her blood.

He comes back from peeing,
dressing gown knotted,
hands in pockets,
grin as wide as the day.
'All right, love.'

Marriage Markets

'But what about his legs, Babaji?
His uncle had such terrible trouble with his legs.
We do not want a grandson with legs like that.'
'I think she'll be fine. Both were straight and strong.'

Mr Singh holds up both hands
to block the views of his wife.
This buzz-buzz of Maya and her men
sucks at his peace like a hungry mosquito.

'Harjit is huge in the Bank. International, they say.
Clever family. His father was in my algebra class.
It will all add up, you will see.'
His mind slips back to his *Times of India* and his tea.

Across the street two six year olds
scrap over a shoeshine rag.
They would eat it
if they could.

'He said he'd ring but I hope he doesn't.'
Laura nods and frowns, sips and puffs
and thinks *you lying cow.* She and Tess have
smoked about six miles of Silk Cut, have put away

a couple of ponds of Chardonnay
down the long years (which get shorter) in bar
after overpriced bar, painting
and repainting a shimmering Impressionist picture of

What They Want. Which is
never to have to go out again,
just stay home with fully contracted men.
Secure, long term employment is their goal.

Taxis cruise down High Street Ken,
headlights slicing the rain,
bearing unburdened women
home to empty flats.

Three miles away, a jacketless youth
who last night emptied his testicles into Tess
prowls his office, sniffing a kill,
growls down the phone at the Bombay dawn,

'Harjit! What's going on there?
Give me the fucking truth!'

Julian Bell is Head of English at Godolphin and Latymer School. His poems are published regularly in magazines, and he is the co-author, with the artist Michael Willdridge, of *A Village Half in Shadow* (Sutton Valence Arts 1998). His comedy scripts have been performed on BBC Radio 4.

Charles Shearer / From the Celtic Fringe

Celtic Dream of Home/ St Ives/ Gleningah Castle Co Cork/ Castle Freke Co Cork

Fred Voss

2 Grease Spots

'Hey that Iraq's gonna think different after we make a grease spot out of 'em!'
says Joe
making his hand into a fist and shaking it up in the air
above his head as if
at the suicide pilot heading that jet toward The Twin Towers.
We're outside the red brick wall of the factory in the gravel parking lot
at lunch
sitting and eating and I look over at Joe
58
years old and not enough money to buy the new glasses he needs
or keep
what's left of his teeth or eat
more than one slice of cheese in his sandwich or keep
a car running or take
a woman out to a movie
and I want to ask him if they aren't making a grease spot out of us too
us men
who have worked our lives away on the machines that made
their world
us men
who can barely put food
on a table for our sons and daughters
us men
who may have to work until the day we die
just to keep a roof
over our head
I want to ask him
if maybe it isn't those people in Iraq who are our enemy
but our own government
letting this happen to us
but I think of the "Proud To Be an American" sticker plastered to his toolbox
and look over at his eyes
desperately glowing
with dreams of glory in a waving flag
planted in foreign soil
that are all he has left
and haven't got
the heart.

Moved in at Last

After 20 years on an Acme-Gridley screw machine
or a Cincinnati milling machine
a man
may inherit the big workbench in the corner of the machine shop
when an old veteran retires
or dies
and the man inheriting the workbench will place his toolbox in the corner
     of the workbench
and then cut a big 1/4-inch-thick sheet of plastic at home
to fit the dimensions of the workbench and bring it in
and cover the workbench with it and begin to slide
photos
under it.
Photos
of his wife in a sexy red dress
his son
with a football in his hand or his daughter
in graduation cap
a big close-up picture of his bare ass a friend took of him with a Polaroid
or his beauty-contest-winning
2-year-old granddaughter
sliding them all under the plastic which he cleans with Windex each day
so all the men who don't have workbenches can pass by
and admire them
photos
of himself crouched in boxing gloves in the ring
or in black leather jacket and pants and hat
on a Harley in 1959
or passed out under the Christmas tree
or with that big 10-foot-long swordfish he caught hanging on a hook
beside him.

After 20 years in a machine shop if he is lucky
a man may begin to feel
like he lives there.

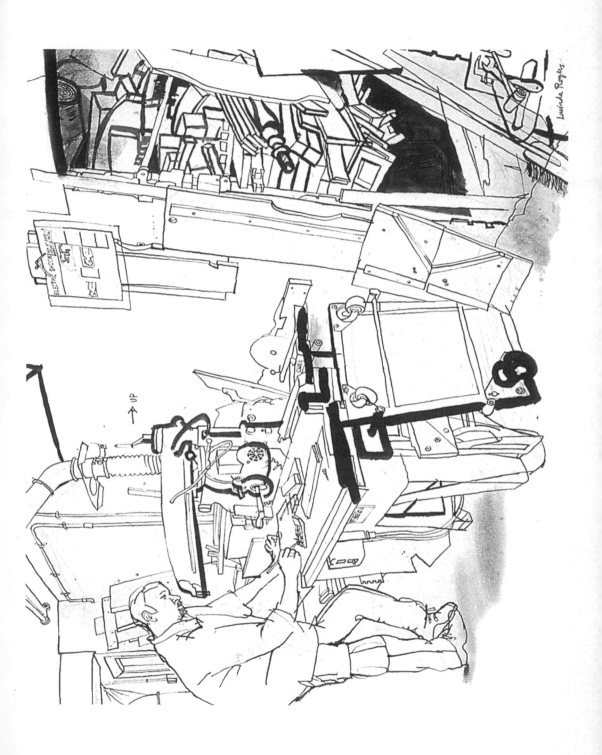

C--ET

Next to me in the gravel factory parking lot at dawn
as I park my car
is a 1964 Comet
driven by the 4 Mexicans who have already clocked into work
not a 'classic car'
some white suburban manager making $100,000 a year
might drive
on weekends as a hobby with every last detail
down to every bit of chrome perfectly restored to as-new perfection
but an old
car with a few dents and the 'om'
fallen off the steel 'comet'
riveted to the rear end
a car
driven by Mario and 3 other machinists who make little more than
minimum wage
and must ride together to survive
a car
shiny with the love that has washed it
and dried it as clean as scrub brush and soap
and chamois will get it
a love
that tunes it on Sundays on some driveway in East L.A.
where every bit of it
has been taken apart and reassembled and taken apart
and reassembled
and rebuilt
and oiled and greased and cared for with hoist
and wrench and feeler gauge and fingers that love the hum of its engine
so that these men
can go on feeding their families
a car
with new spotless tires and a big steel crucifix hanging from its rear-view
mirror
a car
that is somehow what all cars should be
more than hubcaps
and valves and spark plugs and fuel lines and flywheel
a car
with soul.

Eating their Way Through the Walls

On the walls
of this East L.A. neighborhood I drive through on my way to the factory
are vines
green fish serpents
with purple feathers flesh
of senoritas in white dresses suns
full of golden Incan
hieroglyphics on the walls
of these hard brick buildings built by white men a century ago
are leaves
leaves
and fish and serpents and sun in paint
laid across brick by a Mexican man
who maybe works in one of those factories across the river like I do
one of those red brick
factories with walls so hard they squeeze the heart to death
with roaring machines that don't care
and low wages
leaves
and vines so green and suns
so golden and old and powerful painted
with so much Mexican soul
it seems they may somehow soften
those walls
slowly slowly slowly eat
through them
until someday
they have crumbled and fallen along with a world
that breaks our hearts.

Better than Electroshock

Frank
is standing at the window with a beer and all
the pounding
and screaming and shouting and glaring
of the machines and men
from a 10-hour day at the factory is still in his head
as Jane is saying,
'I just think you should always have a couple of dollars in your wallet is all when
you're drivin' that freeway to work and back,'
as she lovingly

slides a bread stick and places a couple of radishes
into the bowl of wonderful turkey vegetable soup
she has worked so hard to make for Frank.
Men
are taunting and cutters snapping in blocks of steel
in Frank's heart even after the beer.
'Are you saying that I couldn't make it in Watts if my car broke down?
Are you saying I couldn't make it to an ATM machine in Watts? Huh?
ARE YOU? ARE YOU SAYIN' I COULDN'T WALK DOWN A SIDEWALK IN
WATTS WITHOUT GETTING BEAT UP AND DRAGGED INTO THE
BUSHES AND GANG RAPED!?'
he roars
as his hand strangles the neck of a beer bottle.

Jane lovingly slides the bowl under his nose as he sits down
and smiles
knowing what an amazing achievement it is to make turkey soup so good
you can drown
psychosis in it.

Fred Voss has journeyed from steel mill blast furnace flame to the 100-foot-long machines of air-craft factories to the red-brick walls of 100-year-old machine shops in downtown L.A., trying to put it all down on the page. His latest collection, *Carnegie Hall with Tin Walls*, is available from Bloodaxe.

Pavlov's Bitch / Nick Sweeney

he others fled from the night in their own ways, and, though she could guess, Carrie never knew what they saw. Only one thing was sure in her night, and that was the road. When she crunched them to a halt, Ivan was out on the red earth of the roadside, clutching his head and rolling from side to side. Ellie fell out of the front passenger seat and, still in heebie paranoia, followed Ivan's movements with her shoulders. Jacob stayed slumped in the back looking a shade of yellow that, Carrie felt, suited him.

Blank, Carrie thought, as he always has been.

Not able for it, she projected at Ellie, and never was. Carrie would graffiti her grave: up for it she was, able for it she wasn't.

And Ivan, he was dead. It hit her that he always had been, ever since the night of the Pearl Jam gig, and then the party in De Beauvoir Town; and after it, when he had given in to the darkness in him and, finding it empty of words, lashed out at her. Dead.

She left them to it, leaned on the jeep, gazed at the water for what seemed like a long time.

Give me a cigarette, Ivan said.

We're out of cigarettes. Carrie relayed it unsensationally.

We're out of everything, Jacob aimed at her.

Carrie watched delicate silver waves break, was about to raise finger and thumb and trap one when Ivan slapped her face. Out of everything, he was saying. His anger delivered the three words in the voice of a child and, like children, they doggy-paddled slaps at each other.

Leave it. Jacob manhandled Ivan away a few paces, unable to say anything but, leave it.

No food, Ivan was calling. I need some fucking food.

No food? Ellie, all anxious eyes, appeared next to Carrie.

Go and buy some. Carrie swept an arm up at the memory of the coastline, at sand and grit and grass and billboards, spiky hedgerows, rusted fencing.

Ivan walked a few paces onto the sand, and began to undress in movements that took on the momentum of a dance. He kicked his pants away and walked, was soon in the sea, gone into the chemistry of wind and water.

Carrie got up and tramped to the top of a dune. She pulled her clothes down and shat liquid, miaowed as she scattered sand over it.

As she stood up in search of another hollow, she heard a grunt of effort, and looked and saw a figure on the beach. Thought it was Ivan at first, then made out a bearded man with a head of thick dark hair. He wore a flowing white shirt, black trousers and red espadrilles. He was hefting boulders across the sand to the dark line of the tide, and he had to be crazy; he was making a circle of standing stones.

***

The evening before, they went to a place whose sole waiter wore the same garb, plus white gloves about three sizes too big. These are our waiters' gloves, son, the boss had obviously said, and if you want to work here then you'll wear them.

The unfilled space at the end of each finger was speckled with every dish into which he had ever plunged them: turmeric, ketchup, olive oil, black brine, the carbon from burnt peppers, it was all there. Their omelettes arrived in bowls whose wells were not big enough to contain them. Carrie wiped a line of oil from the edge of hers into a hollow formed by a glove fingerprint.

Ellie was halfway through hers when she choked, and pointed. The ragged yellow revealed a fatty piece of raw meat in the bottom of her bowl. She freaked and, hand to her mouth, cried out. Ivan and Jacob broke into the outrage over which they had simmered the whole trip.

Carrie said, that one's mine, and swapped plates with Ellie, set about eating the remains of Ellie's omelette.

She doesn't eat meat, Ivan was yelling at the waiter.

Of course. The waiter raised a floppy finger, and an eyebrow, hunched and made a smile that showed promise. He came back in due course with the manager, who listened calmly to Ivan, and Jacob, and noted Ellie's upset face.

Okay, the manager said, and smiled, and went back into the kitchen.

They waited, then stopped waiting, sulked, ate defensively. Carrie's piece of meat was revealed, sour and corrupt as she finished the last scrap of egg.

Jesus, Ellie said. Take it away – get him to take it away, she begged Carrie, and Carrie called the waiter over to do his fingers-and-thumbs part.

God, Ivan and Jacob repeated.

They got out of there without God's help, though not without Carrie's. She studied the bill and asked for it to be corrected, counted the money out patiently. She left a small tip. You had to; it was custom.

***

Outside, two guys were leaning on the jeep. One of them had reached in through the busted side window to take Carrie's Zippo from the dash. He had lit up with it, was by then just playing, making it spark with a jive flip.

Carrie held her hand out for it as the guys straightened up to greet her. The one holding the lighter tried to catch her eye, perhaps to engage her in a boys' game in which she would have to try to snatch it as he held it out of her reach. Her eyes roved instead over the dim interior of the jeep, checked the other windows, the doors: intact; the luggage: unmolested. The guy with the Zippo said something cocky and brave to his mate, who shushed him.

The lighter was put into Carrie's palm. She stowed it carefully in a pocket, and only then did she meet the guy's gaze directly. Hi, she said.

They were conscript soldiers, heading back from leave to a barracks inland. Bodies of men, faces of boys. Their wishes? A broody mix of the two, Carrie guessed. They were squeezed in.

Ellie would sit up front with Carrie, guys all together in the back, spread over the luggage. They got under way. Conversation was sporadic, and led almost directly to the soldiers getting out some puff. They got into the noxious business in the back, drew Ellie into it. Each time Ellie offered Carrie a toke, she said no. She pulled the window up and down, let air in and out.

Maybe three hours later, and running on fumes, they reached a spot at which, the soldiers assured Carrie, they would hook up with pals in a minibus. There was only Carrie to assure; the others were on planet Zonk, poisoned by giggles and happy headache; only Carrie to deal with. She joined them at the back, and, looking somehow taller than they had before, they began.

We gave you something. The Zippo boy indicated the smoky chaos in the back as he and his sidekick got their stuff together. Now you give us, yes? Custom. He seemed very pleased to have found the word.

In our country, the other one added.

We gave you a lift, Carrie pointed out, then remembered a line from the guidebook: that was no gift, was the simple code of the road, and a duty for all who travelled on it.

No, Ivan began to say. That's cool.

Yeah, piped out Jacob. It's only right, man, because this stuff, yeah... it was... right... it was...

Right, right. Ellie took over the show from the chorus with a whoop and a yell and a clap of the hands. Right. Because, when you're... right? When you're...

Stoned, Carrie asked calmly. Despite herself, she too abandoned the business in hand to focus on Ellie, but even the tragic comedy of her friend's confusion couldn't blank out the panic tightening her stomach.

When you are in Rome. Ellie looked around at them all, knelt up on the front seat. You have got to...

She put weight on the wrong knee, fell down and disappeared for a second: show cancelled.

We're not in Rome. Carrie addressed the soldiers. Listen. We're all out of things. Understand?

They shook their heads, tutted.

One of them was about to squeeze one of her little tits, she thought at first, until his hand spread out, and he said, teeshirt?

She was almost tempted to whip it off. That would be a thing to tell his minibus mates about: only man in the regiment to have seen tits other than his little sister's. She said, no.

A present? For me? The other one was pointing at her watch.

Sorry. She made a polite wave at the men. We're out of here.

They moved, but only back into the jeep to go through the luggage. As Carrie watched, they pulled zips open, rummaged in rucksack pockets. Ivan and Jacob watched too. Jacob even pulled his legs out of the way to ease their progress towards Carrie's stuff.

Please, Carrie began. As she took the few steps to the driving seat and back, a travel alarm went into one of the guy's pockets. A toilet bag was opened, chucked on the ground, Ivan's snazzy razor taken, some condoms, flash aftershave from duty-free. Some shades went, a poundshop battery fan. One of them picked up a carrier bag from which oranges dropped. Stop that, Carrie finished. Now.

Her yell gave only the illusion of violence. The reality of it was embodied in the breadknife she held in her hand; a huge thing, dull with the regular markings of the food it had sliced through earlier.

The soldiers took a step away in unison, like a vaudeville double-act, hands wide in gestures signifying innocent outrage. One of them laughed, but Carrie saw his adam's apple marking nervous time.

Cheap, the other one hissed at her, cheap!

What are you, she thought of later, a fucking canary? Her tongue, lips, teeth and palate were all too dry to make the mechanics needed for sounds. She had to find saliva, but didn't want to let the motion of it betray her. She drew stuff up from her throat, and spat on the ground. That did the trick, and then she knew it wasn't just a tough guy bravado seen in films.

Cheap, the canary went on: we give to you, but you don't give to us. Cheap. He signalled the triumph of the word with a closed fist. His mate eyed the knife, and made a you-are-nuts gesture using finger and temple.

Leave. Go. Please. Carrie got the words out, let the knife take up the message, even as the panic inside her latched onto the idea that the brandishing of the blade had committed her to a course of action that, it was possible, would hurt somebody, probably badly, probably her.

Ellie was out in front of the jeep, trying to get the sky to prompt her into finishing her litany. Ivan had come out to lean on the jeep to say only, oh man. He watched Carrie and the soldiers, without seeing them. Dead, Carrie thought, and there she was, about to join him.

Go. Carrie stepped forward behind the knife. Give us our things back and go. Without thinking about it, she picked up one of their kitbags and threw it. It didn't fly far, but its emphatic landing pushed home her wishes.

The Zippo boy seemed about to test her nerve. He bent and put whatever he was holding onto the ground, but then picked it up again and turned. They both jeered, and began to walk away, shedding with crashes and tinkles the clock, the aftershave, the razor. They didn't return everything, though. Private Zippo took the carton of cigarettes out of his shirt and transferred it from hand-to-hand before placing it into the carrier bag full of food. He graced the moment in his best English, embodied in the words, I fuck you.

Go fuck yourself, Carrie called, and she stood there.

What's up now? Ellie was beside her.

Carrie felt that if she relaxed even one little bit, her sphincter would open wide as a dustbin, and she would blow all her internal organs out through it. If she moved any of the muscles in her face, she would cry. She didn't want to cry, and that settled it. Didn't want to breathe, either, but the momentum of the breath she let out empowered her to shove Ivan into the back. She tugged Ellie into the front by a sleeve, and jolted the engine into a cough.

No, Jacob was calling.

Listen, Ivan was trying to say.

She didn't listen. Nor did she stop in time for Ivan to throw up. It was all the body could do, she reasoned, but it would do him no good; the poison was a mushroom cloud in his head. It brought her to a halt, anyway. Jacob hustled Ivan out, and in the act of helping him, joined him in the big hurling contest. Ellie sat there whitely, dragons in her eyes.

Carrie looked at the knife on the dash. She cried then. She looked at the map. She called, come on, at Ivan and Jacob. She put a hand on Ellie's forehead, told her, you'll survive, babe. Looked again at the knife. Was that really her, back there, doing that brandishing thing? It was, she supposed. The soldiers were only a couple of miles back, she sat up and prompted herself; had a minibus full of pals on the way. Christ. She got out and shepherded Ivan and Jacob into the back. She drove.

***

Gulls in their thousands woke her, told her there were fishing boats passing. From high on the dune, the boats floated in the air, she could have sworn, in the glare served up by sun and sea.

Ivan, she remembered, out there naked, kept afloat only by the hollows in his head. When they filled with the revelation of his awesome loneliness, he would sink. A moment of want told her to wade out, wave him in on a trail of shallows she would pick out like magic, tell him she didn't want him to die out there; no way for a vegetarian to go, his face full of feeding fish. It passed. She sank down again, but got up almost at once.

The weird beard stood on the beach in his black and white, ankle-deep in the incoming water, surrounded by his ring of stones. He looked to Carrie like a man at peace with the world; he had finished what he had gone down there to do, and that had to be a good thing: he wasn't dead.

She slept again, woke. The sea was empty of boats, and of fish, too, she supposed, the air empty of gulls. The standing stones were covered, the man gone. Out to sea? Home again to dream up his next weirdo goal? Happy anyway, she had the feeling. She wanted to be happy, too.

She tried to stroll down, lost her footing in places, stumbled. Walking, it came to her, was the art of always stopping yourself from falling. She achieved her stroll as the sand levelled out to make the beach.

Jacob and Ivan were talking in low voices. Ellie: where was she? Carrie didn't care. They were all stumbling, she knew, trying to correct the motion, and failing, and falling – that was their lives. Drive, she thought: that's all I have to do, without stop or stumble, no puking, no cursing, no more customs. Just drive.

Near the shoreline lay a canvas bag. No, a trick of the light: just Ivan's clothes. No: that was the trick, and it was indeed a canvas bag. A rough thing, Carrie saw as she approached it, giving out the look of wet dead weight. She knelt by it, and with some effort tugged its drawstrings apart. It was full of silver. She hefted it onto her shoulder and walked back to the jeep.

You just piss people off, Carrie, Ivan called up to her.

She said nothing.

You get off on it.

All through this trip, Jacob put in, piss people off, and screw things up for us.

Carrie reached into the back of the jeep, took out the bits that made the stove. The familiar noise of the clinking parts quieted them by setting the juices running in their mouths and stomachs, Carrie guessed: they were the Pavlov's dog roadshow.

What's in the bag? Ellie had appeared.

What bag? Jacob got to his feet and joined them.

Fish. Carrie snapped the stove together, held up to the light the precious dribble in the bottle of oil. If she cooked them slowly enough, they would make their own dribble. Sardines, she said.

I'm a vegetarian, Ellie reminded her.

Isn't there anything else, Jacob asked.

No. Carrie almost smiled.

But where did you get them? Ellie looked to be on the point of tears.

There. Carrie gestured at the water. Listen. She thought she might as well try. We're hungry, right?

Yeah, Ellie said, but.

There isn't anything else in the sea to eat. Carrie paused on the edge of the cruelty of it, made her voice gentle. Only fish. She knelt again, set about making the stove ready.

What a bitch, Ivan said.

Pavlov's bitch, Carrie agreed, and smiled at their puzzled silence.

A bitch, was she? Well, this bitch was going to drive them all back up that trail, back to the city limits; she traced the road in her mind for the reassurance it brought: back through the shacks and shanties, back to the car hire place, and goodbye.

You're just going to sit there and eat all those fish? Jacob was standing over her. Just going to sit there in front of us, yeah, and... eat them? And us with nothing?

No. Carrie thought about it.

What, then?

I'm going to eat some of them, and save some to eat later, on the way back.

Back? That was Ivan.

Back. She presented them all with her own back. The first of the sardines were sizzling, ready. Carrie took the breadknife and stuck it under one, drew it carefully to her mouth, and began to eat.

Nick Sweeney writes: " 'Pavlov's Bitch' is a merger of two stories told to me. Anybody who wants the original (but perhaps [and perhaps not] more mundane) stories behind them should contact nicksweeney99@yahoo.com and I'll send you a piece I wrote about them."

Satyendra Srivastava

An Ever Potent God

I grew up
Believing firmly that
Whoever is born
Wherever
Begins to die
Right from the moment of birth
And with him or her or it
Dies the God gradually too
But potent till the last

Today I realised
He lives through all
Witnessing everything
Stone-faced
Smiling blessings and sometimes
Looking right through you

Today I watched
All the wounded
The maimed the disfigured
Being carried away
Bagged or loaded
Into the ambulances
After the blast
In a busy corner of a market

God witnesses all
In my heart of hearts
I believed it then
I believe it now

In the afternoon of the blast
When an almost unconscious
Woman was lying on the ground
Behind a makeshift curtain
As if breathing away her life
After the soldiers had gone away
Laughing shouting
Playing their flutes

And waving their flags
She lay
Surrounded by a crowd
Of men and women waiting for a doctor

And when the doctor entered the place
He ordered everybody to stand away from her
For fresh air and light
And pointing towards the curtain shouted loudly
Lift it up
The woman's body moved
As if she heard the masterly male voice
And she lifted her torn skirt right up to her thighs

God witnesses all
Otherwise she would not have known
The effect on her
Of those commanding words
Lift it up
And obeyed

Because Life must Go On

Becase Life must go on
She said and thundered away
As the light goes off
After the fuse has burnt out

I was only surprised at seeing
That she was wearing
The dress I bought her for her last birthday
And the pink dotted silk scarf
I gave her for her first art work
Which was cutting out a collar
For my torn shirt
And stitching it artistically
And also the scent – sandalwood –
I had bought in Istanbul
After the old wayside perfume seller
Promised and assured me
That whoever would wear it
Would always love me.

That was the day when she said
Because Life must go on
And thundered away
And wore with so much pleasure
Everything I had given her

That day I didn't cry
I don't now either
Because the old perfume seller's words
Keep on ringing all around
Love will never die
And I know
And more so now
That she would not have worn or used my presents
Otherwise
On the day of parting
Five years ago
Exactly

She is married now
Has a boy and a girl
A house a car and caravan
And all the rest
That goes with Life
Which must go on

Blind Games

I am dancing
Inside my blindfold
You perhaps
Are doing the same
Between the sheets
This is our newest game
To avoid the physical
Separate beds
Mine kingsize
And yours
The Queen's

Satyendra Srivastava was born in India but has lived in the UK for nearly four decades. He writes in Hindi and in English. He's latest collection is *Another Silence* (Samvad, 2002). Following his retirement from Cambridge in 2002, where he lectured in Oriental Studies, he has travelled to countries such as South Africa, India, Kenya and Zambia, lecturing and reading his poetry.

Norman Ackroyd / Etchings of Island

On High Island - St. Feichin's Church   Artist proof   Norman Ackroyd / 203

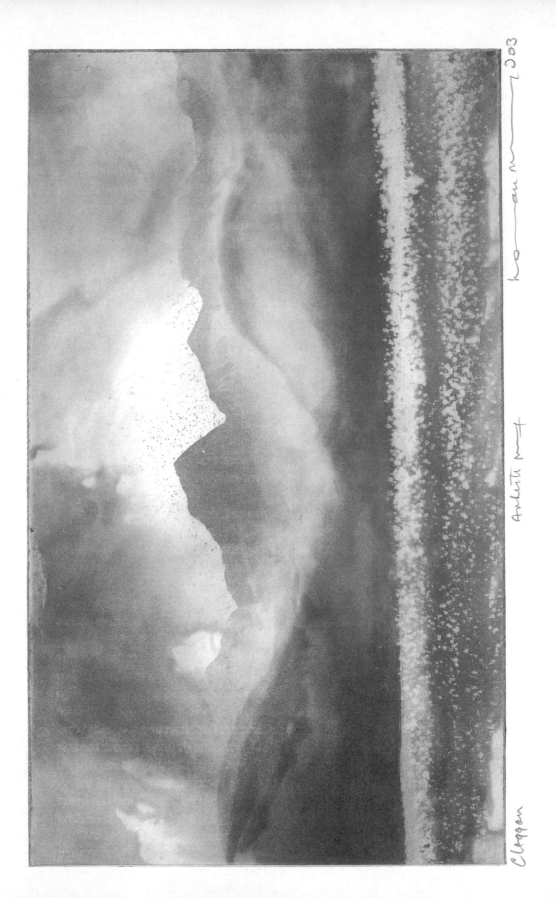

Cloggan

Artists mt

have an interest 003

Croagh Patrick from Ensylatur   Artist proof   Monneur, 2003

Caher Island   Artist proof   [signature] '03

Hairdressers' Picnic / Felicitas Hoppe
trans. Judy Gahagan

The hairdressers come every year in May. We'd like to wear white overalls and wave flags with as much pride as they do. We marvel at their long supple hands and gaze avidly at the huge baskets on their arms, filled with little white rabbits, eggs, wine and pastries.

It never rains when they come. They don't have to look up to know that the sky's blue and that the sun's reflected in their shiny heads. They spread soft cloths out like nets, right beside the lake under the shady trees in the municipal park. They're never in a hurry and they lie like summertime students in the grass, their folded arms behind their necks, with half-closed eyelids. What goes on behind those eyelids we don't know; they don't open any books and they don't leave any notes in the waste bins. We lie flat in the bushes eavesdropping on their innocent breathing until one of them gets up to slaughter the first little rabbit.

The hairdressser's business is washing, cutting, setting, combing, bleaching, dyeing, tinting, conditioning, waving, and spraying to hold the hair firm against the wind, shaving, manicure, pedicure, making up hairpieces and wigs. That lets the little rabbit out of the hairdresser's hairless hand, that we know as well, spies trembling in the hawthorn bush; only when the scissors glitter we shut our eyes tight and press our hands to our ears as if we still hadn't grasped the trick of how everything grows again. Then a hairdresser laughs and waves to us and cracks an egg into the pan.

But there was nothing for us in all this. Eating with baldies brings no luck our grandmother told us and wrinkled her nose as if misfortune was in the air. She cut our hair in her own fashion, with blunt scissors, askew; who needed to look good in such weather. She hung heavy towels over the window when the hairdressers passed by and nailed boards across the door. But we slipped out through the cellar and heard them squabbling behind us as we raced down the street. We couldn't wait, we wanted to look good and we wanted to sit on that soft cloth with no stains or left-overs on it and to join in the feast as at a proper table; for the hairdressers sucked with gleaming lips the meat from the bones until they gleamed like polished teeth. Then they threw them arching high into the lake. Thus did we enter with bated breath into their service.

When evening came on we carried the baskets full of empty bottles proudly. So we wavered a bit, as we went one last time past grandmother's house, the door nailed up and the windows covered; but we could see her quite clearly standing behind the towels with her fists clenched in farewell.

We learned the trade quickly and thoroughly. Over the summer we washed

overalls and ironed them with a heavy iron so that not a crease remained. When the leaves fell we began to cut, comb, colour, bleach until hair fell out into our hands that had become soft and supple as the master's. Mornings we checked our nails for signs of work, for only clean hands could guarantee success in this business.

When winter came our heads got cold, we looked up from our work and saw them shining like cannonballs in the mirror behind the faces of our pale clients. And when it was no longer warm under the covers, of an evening, we told long stories about endless summer by the sea, these were too long for one night for at dawn already the customers stood in front of the door. They banged with their fists on the frosted-up glass and breathed holes in it with their impatient breath. Then they pushed through the door and shoved one another off the chairs as if there wasn't enough room for everyone. The water didn't steam fast enough in the boilers, we sweated and froze between the basins and burned curls around curls and rinsed combs and brushed and mirrors: 'there you are, just look how beautiful we've made you, for Christmas is at the door!' At night, panting, we'd sweep the tiles and clear into the cellars buckets of hair to make wigs like winter hats. When nobody was looking we'd all pull them down over our ears and laugh without stopping at the sight of ourselves in the mirror. But it didn't make us any warmer.

At New Year came the shaving. Now at last we held the knife with its steel blade pliable in its sheath and frothed up the dirty beards. The customers' faces were tired. They stared sluggishly into the mirror and didn't really ask much about the whereabouts of their beards. Finally we poured fresh water onto their faces and smoothed them with our hands. We brushed the last hair from their necks. When we took the white towels from their shoulders they looked good enough to be laid out. They stepped out into the New Year like freshly bathed children who think that spring's coming again. It did come and we took the overalls and carried them into the cellar to be incinerated. We slept furtively next to the stove and dreamed of long journeys in warmer countries, clean-shaven faces pressed up against one another.

But in May we march into town, rucksacks stuffed with rabbits and chickens and anything else we can get hold of on the way. The sky's blue and the girls are waving colourful flags. In the municipal park we put up our tents and get the girls to take off our boots. We lie in their arms and pull their plaits but when we want to kiss them they jump out of the way into the bushes and lie in wait. When the scent rises unmistakably between the trees the girls can hold out no longer. They jump out and get fed and laugh and wipe the grease off our cheeks with their plaits. So we tussle and roll about in the grass as if we hadn't realised that nothing grows again.

Felicitas Hoppe was born in Hameln in 1960 and now lives in Berlin. The 'Hairdressers' Picnic' is from her first book, a highly acclaimed collection of short stories by the same title (Reinbek with Hamburg, 1996). Other work includes a novel, *Pigafetta* (Reinbek with Hamburg, 1999), which was written after a four month voyage round the world on a container ship. See page 5 for biographical information on Judy Gahagan.

Brian Biddle

Copper (Cu)

from Latin Cyprium, from Cyprus

They call me the Cypriot.
My viridian gown clings tight
but you can undress me if you like,
reveal my pink flesh,
so soft and yielding.

Strip me
and I'll accommodate your lone pair
in my empty orbital.
My slim form will coil around you
and the current will surge
with an electric thrill.
We will drift together,
dissolving in Mediterranean blue.

What will I ask?
Neither silver nor gold.
Just take and refine me,
I'm available for a few pence.

See you?

Phosphorus

I can pass in a crowd,
unassuming and mild-mannered
in my old-fashioned brown coat.
You could call me Dr Jekyll.

In the laboratory, a pulse of energy
and molecular rearrangement
will liberate my hidden self,
metastable Mr Hyde.

Released from my confining glass,
I am a pale Lucifer, soft as tallow,
ready to rage and burn,
to strike in one phosphoric flash.

So come closer, factory girl,
come within my grasp.
Let me sear your soft flesh
and disappear in a grey mist.

Silver Bromide

Only where photons
strike a hidden film
will the ions reduce
to a silver stain.

The image formed
from a moment's lapse
through shutter or slit
shows a negative truth –

A missile's dark shadow,
above cratered streets,
may seem to the viewer
an image of light.

But in the emulsion
the wasteland is shot
with atoms of darkness,
a region of night.

Brian Biddle, a retired lecturer and research scientist, continues to plunder science for ideas and has convinced some editors that the gap between science and poetry can be bridged. A collection, *Elements of Surprise*, is in preparation. He is Treasurer of Toddington Poetry Society, founded in 1977.

Winter Kills Love Among Other Things / H.P. Tinker

So, could this be the end for all the post-modern lovers? Somewhere in the season of their wintry discontent... *winter rolling up its sleeves, being endlessly facetious, witty and melancholic, an architect of dreams and nightmares, a social commentator never flinching from caustic observation...*

'We've gone to war,' said Martha (almost-famous for her flared nostrils.)

'Oh,' said Paul (absolutely non-surprised.) *'Have* we?'

'Apparently so.'

'What? *All of us?* Even *me?*'

(Paul was sitting where he always sat. Hadn't, in actual fact, gone anywhere.)

'Yes,' she says. '*You've* gone *too...*'

This was hard for Paul to swallow: he had never taken going-to-war lightly, he nearly always liked to be kept informed about such things. 'Well, you'd think someone might have asked my permission first...' he protested, decapitating an egg with a small shrug, leaving the emotional truth to Martha: *Why?* She's been recently recruited as a Weapons Inspector for the UN and therefore knows more about these things than he does. She talks endlessly about being a Weapons Inspector: their complicated lifestyles, poor diets, limited fashion options... problems commonly associated with being a Weapons Inspector. Often, like a regular pastime, she assassinates the characters of other (more experienced) Weapons Inspectors deep into the earliest of early hours...

Winter at night reflecting the exterior landscape with an air of casual mythic unreality, the undulations of the Yorkshire moors, the jagged cliffs of Cornwall, the polished surfaces of city life, contrasting unyielding architectural supremacy with simple human vulnerability, capturing time and space with the petrified disquiet of a subliminal home video, having spent thousands of years wallowing in a somewhat less than glamorous reputation, now oozing cosmopolitan artfulness into their dreams... 'A dream,' Martha remembered somewhere in the richly seamed season of winter vomiting. 'A *terrible* dream...' The next day, semi-sick with the winter too, Paul asked her about it again. 'I was playing a game of chess with a small grey wolf,' she admitted, '... and losing badly... then the wolf started to grow... and grow... and grow... until... oh, I don't remember the details now...'

Winter pushing on regardless, opening its arms to new lovers, casually embracing all the casualties of winter, those living on the edges where rain falls like footnotes, whose feet take them only in circles... ensconced in winter, like ghosts: a disabled teenager and his over-protective aunts, conversations seldom repeated, presence seldom noticed... 'This winter's gonna be different,' an escaped convict decides, deluded that he can still make it one day, travelling to Las Vegas to discover a cure for insomnia... a roomful of Shoreditch twenty-somethings grappling with Prozac and eating disorders in the basement of the Medicine Bar trying hard to impress at the after-show party... a crippled Irishman, muttering loudly in an otherwise empty field, 'But surely it's never too late...'

Winter refusing to comment, cementing its position only further... congratulating itself on a job well done... overtaking the interwoven lives of a parade of Japanese tourists passing along the embankment and three wayward Armenians: a wine-maker, a writer, a disaffected airport customs official drifting toward prostitution. Their eyes illuminated, all too briefly, by fantasies of sex and violence largely derived from the mass media and the cinema. *Before the sudden, unexpected sickness of winter exploding one night...* which unsettles two impoverished transsexuals in rustic Brazil, shaken by the death of their foster parents... *winter removed once and for all as a potential future spectacle...* for a mixed-race sailor facing up to the meaninglessness of his own, and everybody else's, existence... a popular TV chef, now improbably shipwrecked on a desert island, too much time on his hands. Untold elderly victims of winter falling everywhere; the big freeze freezing all the urgency of lovemaking. Other lovers of winter, then: an unhinged bohemian stealing the husband of her sister... a widow pursued by a philandering dentist and a failed sports psychologist... a Catholic woman and her black gardener consulting a sex manual (...of the listed positions, having previously explored two...) while a teenager's first taste of alcohol has fateful consequences... and the thaw the doctor prescribed never arrives...

Winter shuffling its deck, declining to be drawn on such vagaries, reflecting instead upon the frustrations and anti-climaxes of more sterile buckets of British winter... an ageing photographer mistaken for a hired assassin, whilst on holiday... *winter privately more than pleased with itself...* a widowed psychologist talking impudently to his dead wife on his mobile phone, a Sony Eriksson T610:

'I have turned middle-aged over night.'

'Oh, I do so admire prematurely greying temples, but have you have really aged so considerably since last we met?'

'Yes, it happens. Over time. There's very little one can do about it...'

Meanwhile, a flurry of winter séances. Lights in the sky. Children's voices in the night. The sound of a piano nobody owns. Naked women dancing in a locked room. A one-armed man handcuffed to a bed. A fleet of identical white air balloons taking to the sky. A chocolate giant behaving irresponsibly on the horizon. A strange bird sighted flying over Coney Island. An atheist hairdresser displaying the wounds of Christ.

THE AMERICANISATION OF WINTER?

Winter staying silent on these matters, weighing anchor in various downbeat islands, refusing to accept responsibility for any of the above events, as the cold cuts through like a meticulously maintained scalpel... 'Winter's blunted my formidable ambition, the last remnants of my resolve...' admits a kooky business man (now doing good deeds purely for the darkest of motives). Previously in

love with winter: the snow drift changed *everything*. 'Yes, I would indeed have attended your house-warming party had I been in any way able to...' he confesses into a bathroom mirror... *winter chuckling wryly to itself at all star-crossed lovers and the vanity of their frantic fervour...* the emotional bleakness of a trainee journalist working at an all-black strip club to pay her way through art college. Such are the terse extremities of winter; a highly strung biochemist with a secret past refuses to succumb to yet another:

'Where have we been? Where can we be now? How did it all become so complicated, so corrupted?'

'Well, first there was the fire.'

'Ah, I lost my priceless collection of rare antiquities in the fire.'

'Then came the great big crash.'

'Ah, I lost everything else in the great big crash.'

'But... *Paul Cézanne...* he was noted for his austere handling of spatial forms, was he not?"

'Ye-e-es... but what's *that* got to do with anything?"

Be warned. You may not recognise winter even when it is rubbing up right behind you. Winter often travels under a sheaf of different aliases and holds its real identity close its chest. (Re: two bodies found within minutes of each other. *Who would want to push a cowardly school teacher to his death from a forty-fifth floor window? Who?* And how is this death connected to that of a particularly repellent pornographer discovered in a small lake? *How?*) In this context, the otherness of Eleanor becomes all the more frightening: 'How to disappear completely without leaving a single trace?' she asked me once. I didn't know what to

say. So I charged over on my white charger, in actual fact a pale blue wheelchair. It had been a while since I'd ridden one, and it chaffed between my legs; not making for a comfortable ride, you understand. So maybe white chargers, pale blue wheelchairs, aren't for some people after all. Maybe white chargers, pale blue wheelchairs, aren't everybody's style... *in the*

meantime there's a stumbling figure.
frozen in the landscape of winter.
Immobile for the most part. Moving
occasionally as if to indicate some
general displeasure with these
surroundings. Is the figure bearded?
Badly dressed? Suffering from
horrendously chapped lips? These
minor details are relatively
unimportant, because the figure does
not seem to wholly connect with this
landscape. The irregular textures are
probably alien to them. This is not the
landscape of the past or the landscape
of home. And it is certainly not the
landscape of a brighter future. No, it is
largely unfamiliar terrain, though
certain aspects seem vaguely familiar.
The figure is worried about the terrain,
that it might not support their natural
body weight, causing an unnecessary
stumble, jeopardising the journey
ahead. The otherness of the landscape,
it has to be admitted, is a daunting
proposition. Understandably, the
figure is nervous, standing in this
landscape, unsure of which direction
to travel toward next. Yet when viewed
from a discreet distance the figure
becomes part of the landscape,
absorbed into it... into.... a series of
studied winter vignettes.... scenes of

other winters past, present and future beginning in long shot (a device often employed to suggest 'distance') before zooming into: an illogically minded mathematician packing her car, driven away by the winter... the would-be cowboy from Big Sur almost ready to leave, escaping almost by degrees: 'What drives them to it, we may never know,' assorted members of the Flying Squad comment later, fidgeting amongst themselves... awkward questions lingering in the awesome shadow of the Natural History Museum. Questions that the student film-maker responsible (examining his film sadly, sadistically, rewinding it over and over, taking it apart, putting it back together again) can't really answer, pondering: *What is the broader textual significance of the winter? Where does the thread of winter take these narratives?* Sweating over careful edits and improvisational vividness, his camera roving through the confined spaces of winter... *every story goes somewhere, so where does the sweep of winter take this one? It has to take you somewhere – but where? In a primarily realist and naturalistic narrative, can a story ever match up to the reality of a real situation? Or can a narrative born of dysfunctional parentage avoid the usual problems of fictionalised histories, eventually transcending contemporary forms of desire and consciousness, enmeshing the reader into...* something else, something a little different?: *and can several credible alternate endings possibly be possible at the same time?* (...the beautiful hairdresser who commits suicide... the rehabilitated hero gunned down... the heroine not escaping the guillotine... the babysitter raped by an assortment of former employers...)

'There is only one ending to this film,' the student film-maker realises, much later, only after he's had a lot of time to think about it: an unhappy housewife returning on a poignant February morning, backed by a jazzy Mediterranean soundtrack full of emotional reverberations: her car pulled/dredged from a lake. Cut to: a montage of deformed metal, accompanied by a touchingly wistful hardcore hip-hop beat... *the death of winter? Winter in sombre and reflective mood, on the verge of dropping into the mainstream, having done much of what it set out to do, eavesdropping on the mundane problems of the battered and the bruised...* a retired existentialist now working nights as a wine waiter who mutters: 'Where's my *jeux d'esprit?* I have built a wall around my heart. Erected four tall walls. Fortified it as best I could. Perhaps I was wrong in my judgement, perhaps I was mistaken. But I don't think so. Clearly, anybody could have scaled these walls, had they time and enough rope and the inclination. The obstacles I have put in their way are by no means insurmountable... they were never meant to be... they don't make me completely unapproachable... should I tear down these fortifications right now and erect a white picket fence instead, perhaps?'

Winter looking on despondently... like a troubled troubadour attending his own poorly-attended funeral... finally admitting a small sense of defeat... untold rain falling on the periphery, the outskirts, time moving at a simple and easygoing pace more usually found in the rural South... *winter as obsolete as diplomacy, bureaucracy, hope....*

***

So, whatever became of the post-modern lovers?
'It wasn't as bad as we thought, was it?' observed Martha (eating lesbian jam).
'No, not so'd you'd notice...' agreed Paul (watching the Eskimo Olympics).
'Wars and winters come and go, don't they?'
'Yes, *apparently...*' and with the war over, the winter behind them, the dawn of the Golden Age could finally begin... a short transitory period in world history by all accounts; and another story entirely, as yet untold.

H.P. Tinker lives in Manchester where he has carved a niche for himself as the Thomas Pynchon of Chorlton-cum-Hardy. Born and braised in the North of England (circa 1969), his award-avoiding fiction has appeared in Ambit, emwriting, and Code Uncut among other places, and also at 3am Magazine, where he is a semi-professional editor who writes about soup. Recently, he tripped up in public. Currently, he is incapacitated.

Russell Grant

Mandala
*quaelibet altum cumba pererrat**

Skyline cranes and cable cars,
Approaching Barcelona,

Small freighters, tugboats,
And the Majorca ferry,

Live forefront to the city
And the Royal yacht club.

Fountains and trees
In Plaza Catalunya.

Dripping Gaudi stone
In Passeig de Gracias.

The Palau Musica
Off Via Laietana.

Outside the Town Hall,
They dance the Sardana.

It was ninety degrees
All the way to Barcelona;

Ninety-five degrees,
The week I waited.

We sailed after a storm,
The sea jostling,

And Bohdan braved it:
And came to Vilanova.

***

Ten miles inland,
The rambling house,

* *'Any little craft now wanders at will upon the deep'* – *Ovid*, Metamorphoses
  (Horace Gregory, Viking, NY)

Huge vaults and presses
From the sixteenth century,

Tiled floors and staircases,
Ochre yellow, midnight blue,

And a splashing fountain
In an inner courtyard.

Scattered vineyards,
Green mountain finery.

Snakes in the pine forest.
Sea glimpses beyond the valley.

  ***

The months of the summer
Passed in reflection.

Catalan, English, Spanish,
Friends, artists, acquaintance.

Wine glasses emptied,
Pan tomat and aiole,

Plates of courgettes and pasta,
Al fresco on the broad terrace.

Long past midnight,
Late evening supper debates.

Sitges cathedral
On a hill by the sea,

Narrow white streets
In the town below,

And a tree-lined promenade,
Decorating miles of beach.

A bare blue sky,
Scintillating.

Languorous
Grey-blue sea,

Grovelling at the feet
Of paddleboat men;

While listless waves
Fall fragile on the sand,

In much the same rhythm
As punkah wallahs,

Long used to determine
The measure of some far infinity.

***

It was not such an end
As I felt I could finish,

A smooth ride from Sants
Undid months in a day.

North in the Metro,
North in the Tube,

And a winter passed, and Spring.
'Mandala' in Vilanova.

Reaching home, discouraged
By the popularity of the sun,

Clinging to thoughts of fierce tides
And rough channels off Britanny.

Reading, writing, radio,
And The Wall tumbling,

And no dream succeeding,
I set out to retrieve myself.

I set out to retrieve my boat,
Willing a new apocalypse.

***

Instead of cruising 'Mandala', Russell Grant met Susan and triangulates between London, St. Louis and le Continent. He is a fully paid up member of St. Louis Blues' Society at B.B.'s 'Jazz, Blues, and Soups', also 'Broadway Oyster Bar'. He has published *Essays on Anxiety* (ELSP, 2001) and is looking for a publisher for a collection of London Poems.

A Compression of Distances
The roof bosses of Winchester Cathedral on our 20th wedding anniversary

We could, I said, hold
one in our hands: trace
how the stone leaves
are entwined like held

hands. And then, you said,
see how the boss holds
the roof's ribs of stone, how the lines
open out and gather speed.

Like the early universe, I said,
expanding faster and faster
towards light years.
The geometry of space, I said,

and the curving of galaxies.
Then think about our space,
you said, and the curve of our bodies
together. Suddenly

our anthem, Mozart's *Ave verum*,
rose through the stone spaces
compressing time
and distance. Intersections

of time and stone held us.
Think of the word games we've shared,
all the stories you've told me, the rich ways
of our life, I said... Look how each knot

of stone is an ease and complexity of leaves.

Dark Matter
The visible universe accounts for no more than 4.4% of the whole, and unknown 'dark matter' is believed to surround galaxies with its gravity

There it is, you see,
the dark barn in Rembrandt's nativity scene,
halo of darkness round
the centre of light.

What kind of person would think more of unlit walls,
invisible dark air, than of that light
from the baby, shining like the elation
of a child who goes higher and higher on a swing?

Then there's his reflected glow falling
on Mary with her composed
quiet gaze, and on the shepherds,
concentrating, at the edge

of darkness. But the unseen
barn holds them all together,
has infinite possibilities
in the rich browns shading to black.

It's a peopled dark, it hides
those bounding lines you show me always.
It's peopled like our joined souls
with their unknown linkages and secret

webs of words surrounding
our galaxy of days,
that bright centre held
by what is closed to sight.

Laughing at Gravity

Such a bully it was, that force
gravity, getting tough on what resisted.
Newton's apple cracked
many a head,

like the force coercing
loveless families, like the force
that ruled peoples and
subjugated lands.

Now we have lines and surfaces,
dents in the fabric of space,
curves, the benign
discipline of space-time.

It couldn't be otherwise, we say.
As we lie in bed, our bodies
making twice the dent of one
in our patch of space,

two books slither to the floor, land
with a thud... an unstable
pile of books topples
while we laugh at gravity,

at ease with configurations, turning
'necessary' into 'home'.

Daphne Gloag read Classics and philosophy at Oxford but worked mainly in medical journalism and editing. Her poems have been broadcast and widely published, and she won first prize in the 2001 Poetry on the Lake competition. Diversities of Silence (1995) was published by Brentham Press. She is married to poet Peter Williamson.

Henry Cleverly
Render My Heart
Laundry Press (no price)

It doesn't feel quite right to offer a critique of such affable and sincere poems as these. There's so little pretension in them. But anyway: after reading these poems I began to suspect that the weird non-sequiturs in many of them were resulting from a hit-and-run approach to imagery and to syntax; that, given the faintly mystical and abstract topics and the elevation of tone that such topics invoke, it seemed like the author thought he could get away with it. Here's an example, from 'Elijah':

...there are stones and bushes
in the scrub of thought

I say that words
stop at nothing

churning but to butter
sticks to snakes

and raven's talk
I would not utter

but someone must answer
the bird of this song.

And another example, from 'Out On the Longest Curve':

But what was learnt
at the edge of the mind
where we mislaid our pipe and drum?

A bud turned to flower
without a word
the world dropped away...

...and so on. Or a typical poetry workshop nightmare, from 'The Proof of the Pudding':

Everything expresses itself
when simple things stop doubling up
and become as they were

before they became difficult
nothing can ever be the same thing twice
beyond that carry on, confusion is
confusing... the message we drum on the window
is an urgent dub
the power of philosophy

Why would a poet lead the reader into this kind of conundrum? Probably because he/she couldn't dissipate sufficiently the haze surrounding the thought but went ahead anyway. When he focuses on the description of the place of a poetic moment then poetry emerges, as in the poem 'Winter':

trees blur
purple silver birch
ips turn into smoke

a bonfire sends up
dank atmospheric references
wet bark, gnarled roots

Autumn ploughed
into the ground.

The land
loams dark to the ditches

a horse stands iconic
full of itself
known by its markings

Judy Gahagan

Vuyelwa Carlin
Marble Sky
Seren £6.95

These poems range across worlds – geographically from Africa to America to northern places generally; and they travel in mood and tone from the literal/prosaic of 'Bottles of Blood' and 'Polish Wedding' to the refined bleakness of 'Cold Places' or 'Jezyk Polski'. They are all rich in imagery, ideas and experience. However I found it was the 'northern' poems that harvested the most poetically committed, most intense poems. For example, 'Look on my my Works':

Snowy paths
and the birch trees – such beauty,
whispering over closed souls,
souls like stones
presenting no doors: those smiles
those absences terrible

It is in these poems there's a purity and intensity to rival Louise Gluck's. Take 'The Shadow':

The long shadows of evening, how beautiful!
the shadow of us, how ambiguous:

the deep wracked garden
where only God walks –

touches dark boles, but beyond knowing.
– What are we, at the roots?

...or the wonderful 'Fear of the Wind'.
　　　But there's another theme stalking the
group called 'The Marble Sky'. The poems here
refer to her disabled son; they realise poetically
the intransigence of a strange consciousness.
'The Marble Sky':

Opaqueness; block world;
I glimpse your landscape, bump against its
　　　　　　　　　　　　　word-casts –

in your nineteenth year, Father Christmas
still teetered on frosty tiles, scrabbled in
　　　　　　　　　　　　　chimneys.

The curve of time; the odd loopback
– fizz of future-present:
is that why densities charmed, weighting the
　　　　　　　　　　　　　palm?

　　　There is scarcely a poem here that's not fully
and intensely realised. These are poems for the
collector – to be read and re-read. **Judy Gahagan**

Peter Dale
Under The Breath
Anvil £7.95

I'm not quite sure of the line between the full-
blown elegy and the poem of memory – often
regretful – that risks the 'down-memory-lane'
treatment in which intensity of sentiment
becomes smoothed over by the literal and
facetious. The first three poems in this collection
'Answer', 'Visitation' and 'Nocturne' are
breathtaking. The unguarded intensity of feeling
is transformed by a precision of voice expressing
this feeling that has created three truly great
elegies. The poems that follow these three, still
elegiac, don't sustain that purity and intensity of
tone. Here's an extract from 'Answer':

Oh, slowly answer, my phlegmatical,
from what you do in your unruly flowers;
with that sense of timing, always yours,
avert the angry impatience of a second call.

...and from 'Visitation':

So cool this moss;
cool as your hands were, always,
even in your raving.

I have laid you living
and, in this cold, cold place,
I would lay you dead –

...and from 'Nocturne':

This dateless day is inching to an end.
I cannot summon a cry, as child I could,
nor hold the light up longer in my mind.

　　　A few pages on we have the regretful irony
about the age to which the elegy so often
belongs, but now facetious and busy like this
from 'Soliloquy of an Elderly Child-Minder':

Old men, you bet, will garrulate,
spieling some know-how for a whelp
like you to lap up as self help.
Not me. Best take experience straight.

...or simply conventionally wistful like this
from 'Wishful':

The walks we shared.
Remember that view;
mossed, dry-stone walls
like veins in kail.
How far we saw
from our high hill.

Or simply that the moment becomes too slight
as in 'Orchard'.
　　　Some of this decline can be traced to an
insistence on strict rhyme schemes that straight-
jacket what might have been sifted from the
poetic moment. On the other hand his fluency
and skill, his sure-footed diction, are a pleasure in
themselves. Take this, from 'Mottled':

From long distance here
I'm speaking to you. I beg you do not catch
my words made clear,
like footprints in a night of snow unheard
a wind-rattled latch,
but out of place and time I give you my word,
broken all other ways,

that when you see wet pigeons now you'll
dream
a line in rain that vanishes in haze,
wake to a wordless scream.

...and his perfectly chosen sestina 'Hearth-Light'.
Nevertheless when rhyme constraints are abandoned he returns to the spareness and focus at the heart of an elegiac thought – 'The Last Word':

Just you remember the wild cherry,
stranger, this grey cloud piling.

With it, I've harried the darkness,
fixing its last green particle.

Now it will hold in your mind's eye,
proof against you and your hindsight,
skulk where you will, my dead ringer
tolling the hours that were steadfast.

And similarly with 'Misencounter', apart from the faintly archaic and therefore stilting of "time's offence" and "eye of memory" he returns us to the refinements of the first three poems.
Judy Gahagan

Sheen
Peter Redgrove
Stride £10.00
Full of Stars Dreaming
Various Poets
Stride £5.95

Peter Redgrove, who died this year aged seventy-one, has left us this final collection, *Sheen*, to show that there was no diminution in his creative powers as his life drew to a close. From the beginning of his career he has been an original and unusually prolific writer and, at his best, he could achieve effects which few other poets could rival. What always fascinated and inspired him was the inherent magic of ordinary experience and phenomena and his poetry contained a kind of pantheistic celebration of the physical world and all its furnishings. In *Sheen* we find not only rain, wind and various flora and fauna recreated and celebrated, but a psalmodic account of a men's public urinal.
Redgrove was, in his role of shaman and verbal alchemist, a profoundly serious poet, but he was not a solemn one. The vein of humour

and wit frequently appear in *Sheen*, as in most of his work, and they prevent the intensity of thought and feeling from becoming oppressive. However, I don't think he is a poet to be taken in large doses. There is too little variety in rhythm and the verse-form he chose to use here and in most of his later work depends too much on typography and pays too little attention to the musical possibilities of poetic structures. While his sensuous imagery can often be vivid and accurate he sometimes strains too hard for his effects as here, in 'The Grey Boat', where that "ironing themselves" is clumsy and lacking visual credibility:

Seagulls folding themselves
out of the sky
like clean napkins
Ironing themselves
alight on rooftrees
as for a mile-long banquet

Redgrove's visionary celebrations of his physical and metaphysical worlds might not be to everybody's taste but there can be no denying the originality and richness of much of his work to which eloquent tributes are paid in *Full Stars Dreaming*, a small anthology of poetry in praise of the man and his poetry. The contributors include, among others, Phillip Gross, Andrew Motion, Peter Porter, and John Burnside who has produced two poems of quite extraordinary beauty and technical accomplishments which alone would be worth the price of the book.
Vernon Scannell

Night Toad – New & Selected Poems
Susan Wicks
Bloodaxe £8.95

Susan Wick's *Night Toad* is a substantial volume, very nicely produced by Bloodaxe, containing a new collection under the book's title along with generous selections from three earlier collections, *Singing Underwater* (1992), *Open Diagnosis* (1994) and *The Clever Daughter* (1996). The poems are presented in reverse chronological order, though I rather doubt that a reader would be able to infer this from an undated text, for there is not much change in either form or the preoccupations that supply content. The poems are, on the whole, well made and if they lack lightness of fingering it could be argued that the absensce of the lyric note is appropriate to the bleakness of vision that informs so many of them. This bleakness does not preclude quite frequent flickers of quirkiness and wit, but the dominant mood is of a fairly dark shade of grey, and a brooding awareness of the remorselessness of age and mortality is not often absent.

However, this sometimes oppressive preoccupation with pain and the depredations of time does not mean that *Night Toad* is a book to be avoided. On the contrary, this poet possesses a distinctive talent and is able to write poems which, in part or in their entirety, stick like burs to the memory. In 'Fishing-Boat, Aldeburgh', for instance, the opening images are vivid and achieved with admirable economy:

Red roof, bright turquoise hull,
this little fishing-boat puts out to sea
in a confetti of wings. They float up
to scatter themselves again, a fluttering
                                    marriage
of sea and sunlight, the boat's live wake.

And here is the end of the haunting 'Blind Skiers':

They lean out into the valley
where a sprawl of villages
sleeps already in starlight.
Under their feet the moguls
flex curves of dark muscle.
Black snowflakes melt against their faces.

Susan Wicks has been on the poetry scene for a relatively short time and it will be interesting to see in what direction her undoubted gifts will next take her.
Vernon Scannell

The Book of Matthew
Matthew Welton
Carcanet £7.95

This is Mathew Welton's first collection but it is not the work of an apprentice poet who lacks the skills and know-how that enable him to find his own voice. He is in his mid-thirties, edits the magazine Stand, and is a lecturer in Creative Writing, and *The Book of Matthew* is an assured performance from a writer who has mastered his craft and displays a command of versification

that is becoming regrettably rare among today's claimants to the title of Poet.

One of the attractive features of Welton's work is in the way in which he shows a wise mistrust of abstraction, conveying ideas and emotions through concrete images. He is clearly fascinated by the ludic possibilities of verse-patterning and the title-poem is a set of thirty-nine variations on an original ten tercets, an exercise which I found finally too repetative to hold the full attention for the whole course.

This kind of virtuosic performance, while impressive in its way, offers the reader too little reward for the demands it makes, and the slight shifts from statement to statement do not carry the kind of significance that the poet, by presenting them under rubics taken from the classifications of Roget's Thesaurus, rather pretentiously seems to claim. And if you find that confusing, you should try reading *The Book of Matthew*.

Another disconcerting thing about this collection: a rather fine poem called 'Van der Kerkhoff' on page 11 appears again, unchanged, on page 17. This would seem like a production error but on Page 24 a poem under the title 'DeBoer' turns out to be yet another printing of 'Van der Kerkhoff' except for a small change in the penultimate line, and then, bewilderingly, 'De Boer' turns up again on page 32 with a minor change – a hyphen in place of a comma – in the penultimate line. Because of Welton's irritating and Ashbery-like trick of giving many of his poems titles which seem entirely unconnected with the texts, and the general playfulness of much of his verse, I am still unsure whether these doppelganger pieces are intentional or not.

The *Book of Matthew* contains much that is enjoyable and a good deal that is maddening. On the whole an unignorable debut.
Vernon Scannell

Sue Butler

Teaching History

On the pad by the hall telephone
she finds a London number and beneath it
what might have been a blue biro heart
before it was coloured in, disguised
as an isosceles triangle.

Today Lenin would have been 133
and strolling down South Molton Street
in his waistcoat and single breasted suit
he would not have stood out in the crowd.

She uses her finest Earl Grey
and to give it an edge, cuts
two thin slices from an Armenian lemon,
adds a generous finger of Scotch.
Like the plate on which she puts the biscuits,
speckled with raisins and milk chocolate chips,
she made the cup herself.

The voice of Woman's Hour anchors the day.

Like the daughters of king Danaus,
who for killing their husbands
were condemned in Hades to pour water
eternally into a bottomless vessel,
she knows there is nothing she can do,
nothing she has the energy
to even attempt to change.

Mostly they just do not talk about it.

He tells the other women
whatever they want to hear.
She teaches history
and sometimes at the weekend
smokes the occasional joint.

Murder

You have taken bread, a sweater, suede gloves and the thick, felt boots
that swaddled your legs the afternoon we walked here
from Psokov, carrying all we owned.

Both Plinys are gone. Also Mahler and Leonard Cohen.
I would weep if I were not so tired.

I have been out buying milk for under an hour
so you must have had help to have taken down six flights of stairs:
skis, sheet music, violin, the glass tank with its plastic mermaid
and ribbons of green polystyrene weed.

You have left one of the goldfish in a pickle jar,
the pickles and dill on a saucer.

I hold the jar to the lamp for the hundredth time, smell vinegar
etching scales and fins, marvel
at Blake's wild colours, Dürer's Renaissance precision.

Unfortunately, this fish is dead.
You should have said you were unhappy.
You could have chosen a warmer, less windy day, saved yourself
all the hurrying.

Going Back

I let you pour wine, but do not drink it, can think of nothing kind to say,
so say nothing. You look... I do not care what you look like.

This kitchen is the bare Beckett stage where I almost drowned
in the soups and rich stews of a dream I had waited so long to make real.

I tried to leave a dozen times, but I lacked the power; learned fear
is a whirlpool, an ancient god with great jaws that lock.

You were busy making money to secure our old age, and when I cried
here it was softly, so as not to disturb you or the neighbours.

Sue Butler currently lives in Hertfordshire. She has travelled widely in China, Russian, Uzbekistan, Sri Lanka and Malaysia. *Vanishing Trick*, her first full collection of poetry, is due out from Smith/Doorstop in Spring 2004.

John Emanuel / Figures and Cornish Headlands

John Emanuel lives and works in St Ives in Cornwall and exhibits widely throughout the UK.

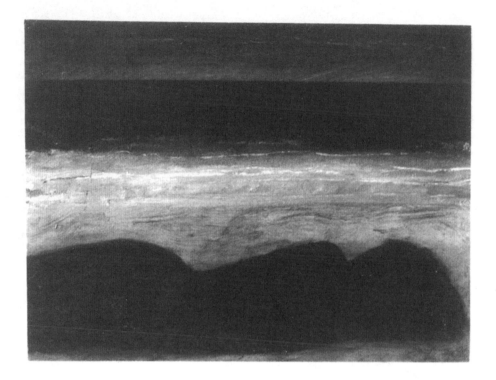

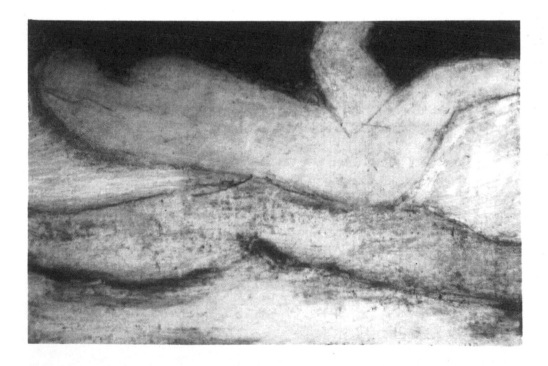

Joan of Arc

i.
They begin,
small whispers which round my ears.
See; I am doing it myself,
turning in my vision,
turning it in to the mad orbit of days.
They begin,
with their sleight of hand,
thrusting me into tight corners of space.
I say, I cannot be alone with these things,
these thoughts which spill
into each musty corner.

I am silent and unmistakably sheened,
with my mouth lapsed open.
They speak, in vast curls of roundness,
in mixed lyricism.
My ears are buzzing with the feel of them,
and the ache of the flames crawling higher.
They are oozing through the cracks in my door,
their oily presence.

And so I cut off all my hair
and fit myself for battle,
naked and glowing beneath
the looped casings of my armour.
No longer silent, I am speaking in tongues,
loosing my mouth with good wine
like the soldiers do.
So I spiral higher. Let the battle commence.

ii.
So they gather the dead rushes into crude bundles,
tying the ends with hair and spun thread.
The pyres are built with care,
the songs of the builders drifting over to where
I kneel in my shift, more girl than warrior.
My eyes are raised to my own sacrifice
as they douse the pyres with oils and perfumes.
The mouths of the priests are wet with mead,
my own starved lips mouth my endings.

And so they lift me like a prize, these glazed men,
and call upon their faiths to carry me away
on their burning fronds, their conscience.

The flames lick my thighs, my own scent hangs and cloys.
And it scares me, oh it scares me
when I see how men fall and flay themselves
at my feet like penitent saints or cracked gods.

Rapunzel

From my tower I can see
the tops of the far trees.
I can see them coming,
one by one,
these half dead men.
Curiosity fires my blood,
and I burn like a beacon
in my high room.

Sometimes they come in twos,
and lie in wait,
avoiding each other's eyes.
Rapunzel, they say,
let down your hair.
And so I do.
I do as my senses bid.

My charmed locks fall,
grazing their faces, and they climb.
Each one is more trusting than the last,
each one is more sure.

My daring grows,
drawing them in with
octopus feelers.

The Frog Princess

This heart pounds and mocks.
I pull on my frog-skin gear and
wish for someone to turn me into a princess.
Following sluttish nights the
aftershock leeches like a sick thing.
The payback.

I open my eyes to a newly sullied world.
I think this is the answer
but after the pretty boy's kisses I am still a frog.

Melissa Collin, originally from the Saddleworth moors, now lives in Norwich. She went to the Norwich School of Art and was published in early editions of Birdsuit. She works as an editor for a local publisher and, after a pause, has just begun to submit her own writing to publishers again.

Performance Reviews from No Man's Land
/ Mark Peebles Brown

At night they broadcast commercials. Actually, I don't know for sure it is them, it could be us. Anyway, somebody broadcasts them, the same ones over and over again. At night distraction is king. Matt Silk and I talk and play Mattel football with the sound muted to take our minds off the commercials. Silk is struggling; he's having trouble at home. One of his kids has Down's Syndrome and his wife blames him for not being around. She thinks he's at a sales conference. She thinks he's entertaining clients at Hooters. He thinks she's sleeping with everyone.

Presentation binders flap through the air over our heads. Outgoing. The shelling is in support of our attack. We are doing a flanking maneuver, we always do a flanking maneuver.

They know it's coming and we take heavy casualties. Jones from Shipping. Matt Silk. I remember he had a sign on his cubicle, in the days when we had cubicles: *What part of 'No' don't you understand?* The whistles call retreat, and I leave Silk, pretend I don't see him. He's grossly overweight and will slow me down.

***

Later, I worm through the labyrinth of trenches and bunkers looking for Ed and Willie. I hunker down and slosh through the mud, not caring that my suit, Hickey Freeman, is getting ruined at the cuffs. I find Little Willie sitting on a sandbag, kicking his legs like a schoolgirl.

'Thank goodness I found you, they want you and Ed in Marketing.'

Machine gun fire crackles out in No Man's Land. Whistles blow, far off. Not our division.

'Yell-o.' Willie says the word repeatedly, like trying a combination lock. 'Yeah-low. Yell-o-wah!'

Willie hits me with a barrage of yellow, so I take off – I am on a mission. I'm supposed to find Ed and Willie and tell them something, or was it bring them somewhere? I forget.

I find Ed in a forward gun position. He's slumped in the mud like only a dead guy would slump. I turn him over. He's riddled with Sharpies, a whole multi-color pack. 'Bastards!' They even removed the safety caps.

All I can think of is that Ed will never straighten that slice out now. Ed died a slicer.

Bruce, Accounting too, comes up behind me, 'Ed?' I nod. 'Shit. Well, it could've been worse.'

'How could it possibly have been worse?' I ask him.
'It could've been me.'

***

In the trenches, we take everything we can get our hands on. Like water, the best place to carry drugs is in the body. No one has heard from HQ lately. There is a lot of talk. Who ordered this birthday cake? Where do all these drugs come

from? The drugs are a godsend though; they make worries like these just float away.

At night, during the commercials, I think about my kids. I sing to myself, a song I used to sing them about a man who sees his lover's face in the reflection on a snow-covered mountain. I sang this to them, selfishly, so that when they see a mountain they'll think of me. And so, when they have a really tough problem, they can just look at a hill or snow or a thing that reflects other things and it'll remind them they're not alone. Sometimes at night I see their faces on the white mountains that lie beyond the enemy pillboxes.

Deeper in the trenches, I find Jimbo, on loan from the International Division. He's brandishing a label gun indiscriminately. The safety is definitely off, because red labels are spitting all around.

Whump!!

An HP LaserJet II slams into the ground in front of our foxhole, showering us with dirt and plastic paper tray shards. Jimbo jumps up, screaming, 'Die, cocksuckers, die!' and sprays labels into No Man's Land. The wind flutters them back at us, and I read them as they snowflake down. Pow-Wow. Mangle the Guru poodle cup. Finalize the win-win situation. The marketing secretary has huge tubes and a tight package. Strategize the follow-up meeting. Pow-Wow (again).

Here, I sort of lose my shit and laugh uncontrollably as I slip into a daydream I keep having. I am on KP and we're serving a choice of either langoustines or rat. I am cleaning the langoustines, breaking them in the middle and tossing the shrimpheads in a garbage bin and then the tails in after them. There's nothing in the langoustines pot, so everyone orders rat. Martha Stewart is there too, dressed as Annie Oakley with six-shooters and fringe, the whole nine yards, shelling the langoustines along side me and giving pointers on how to grill them.

When I get hold of myself, I set out again. I have to tell Joe Haskell about Ed and Willie. This will not be good. I head back through the trench system. It is a hub-and-spoke design, with Marketing as the hub. At the hub, I find Joe Haskell in the Situation Room pouring over battle plans. He slides red and blue pieces on a boardmap with a long stick and punches formulas into his HP-12C calculator. Joe is an inspiring sight, slicked black hair, expensive retro spectacles, red power tie in a crisp Windsor – you can tell he's never felt more alive than in this very moment.

At first Marketing used a Risk board for our planning sessions. And we marveled at the marshalling of forces and the plans with arrows and pincer movements sweeping across the Eurasian theatre. We used Irkutz as our base of operations for a hub-and-spoke system on a grand scale. There was buy-in from all departments. Then, after the first operations failed to achieve their objectives, we right-sized and switched to a roadmap and those little green army men. But it was too confusing with our guys and their guys both being green and all. Now, we just use a regular Stratego board.

Joe Haskell takes the news of Ed and Willie very hard. He flings the Stratego board against the side of the bunker. Blue and red pieces fly about dangerously, with all those sharp corners.

'Well, you're senior accountant now,' he tells me. 'You fucking deal with the paperwork.'

Joe never used to swear. According to the manual, it is strictly forbidden in the workplace.

Joe grabs his rifle and helmet and jumps on the Situation Room table. He peers down at all of us, support staff, tired guys lying against the wall, marketing analysts, guys with earphones receiving and relaying critical information.

'All right everyone, listen up,' he shouts. 'Rustle up a gun. Ammunition. We are taking that hill!'

He has a gleam in his eye. Joe sees himself as a man who takes hills. He has an MBA from a top school, he is a wiz with PowerPoint, he makes appropriate hand gestures when he speaks. And he runs out of the bunker. We look at each other with flittery rabbit eyes. We follow Joe Haskell. I run with them, yelling 'Yeah!' and 'Kill!' like they do. You just have to get psyched up for climbing out into No Man's Land.

Joe Haskell stops at Little Willie's sandbag. Words are exchanged. He's trying to get Willie to buy into his impromptu take-the-hill plan. I'm too far back to hear, but I see Joe's face redden and spittle fly. Then Joe runs on, I guess spitting on Willie was draining the momentum of our attack. As we run by, Little Willie shoots us in the back. 'Grrrr-een. Ba-loo!'

I trudge along behind the pack, then duck into a corner. I take out a company logo pen and pad. I have to write Ed's performance review; I feel the weight of the responsibility. But sitting here now, I can't think. What can you say? What did my last review say? Shit! I've never written one of these; I am not qualified for this. *Ed worked well with others.* Yeah, that's good. *Ed took on responsibilities beyond the roles and responsibilities of his job.* No, not good, can't use responsibilities twice like that. What's another word for responsibilities? Roles? Fuck! *Ed always came to meetings with an extra pen.* Excellent! *He was a good soldier, even though he wasn't supposed to smoke in the forward gun position, which was probably why the sniper hit him with the Sharpies. Worked well with others.* Rolling now. *Soft and filled with squishy red tubes and sacs dying to get out. A wellspring of ideas for improvements and efficiencies we'll never know.*

Overhead, the hideous screech of faxes.

'Incoming!!!'

I smush further into the corner of sandbags. I look off and try not to think about the shelling. The mountains in the distance are tall and abrupt. They rise up confidently, miles past the battle, like they're reaching up to pull down the sun. I don't recognize them. I have never seen these mountains, even in pictures or movies or books. They are foreign, alien, they cannot possibly be ours. Who's are they? Where the *fuck* are we?

I drop the pad. I throw the company pen into No Man's Land and slide down in the mud. My boss, Joe Haskell, used to come into my cubicle, back when I had one, and ask me to do things, and he'd promise if I did them everything would be great. 'That would be great,' he'd say, like a mantra or a magical incantation. Well, I did them. I always did those things for Joe. But you know, that's just it, nothing ever did turn out great.

Mark Peebles Brown splits his time between London and Virginia. His short fiction has won awards and appeared in literary journals in the US and the UK.

Valerie Clarke

The Golden Horse, Neruda Street, Prague

(The quotations in this poem are from poems of Jaroslav Seifert, taken or adapted from Ewald Osers' translations.)

Neruda – each syllable a caress, thought Pablo,
appropriating it to make a name more famous
than Jan, poet of Mala Strana, district
where I sleep under beams at the Golden Horse,
house of no lift and many stone steps.

En route for the church of St Nicholas,
I stop for black coffee and schnapps
near a second-hand bookshop,
skate across poems by Jaroslav Seifert: –
'I have a window, a Spring day floats in it
like a boat with a pink flag on a river...'

Night.
Wheels thump on cobbles under my window,
the entrance door hums at the hostel opposite.
Above are woods of the Petrin Hills, the Castle,
and rising behind old houses, a church,
its clock chiming the quarters.

The garbage truck wakes me at seven.
I take a shower in the cool bathroom
thinking of him, survivor of two world wars,
the Stalinist stranglehold, poems copied in samizdat,
printed abroad after Prague's brief Spring.
'...Those beautiful nights when the city resembles
a rose, a chessboard, a violin, or a crying girl...'

Something of how his life might have been
I find at the Museum of Communism
housed in a pink and white building:
Casino Palace Savarin – (incongruous bedfellows).
I'm no gambler, take the tram home,

open his poems, my notebook. Would he object
If I borrowed his images, sifted his thoughts?
I imagine he enters, props his stick against the door-jamb.
'...Events themselves hand the poet a ready pen
that with its tip he may indelibly tattoo his message
not into the breast but directly into the heart...'

Author's note: Jan Neruda (1834 - 1891) Poet and author of *Tales of the Mala Strana*. The Chilean poet, Pablo Neruda borrowed his name as his nom de plume.

Canal Gardens
Adapted from Ewald Osers' translation of Jaroslav Seifert

Count Canal de Malabaila (1745-1825) founded the Canal Gardens in 1790 in the Vinohrady section of Prague. It was a botanical garden used for experimental scientific purposes.

In old age I've learned to love silence,
she holds more shells to the ear than music.
Forgotten names float through the brain's cosmos,
signals appear on crossroads pointing new routes.
At dusk I've sometimes heard the heartbeats of birds,
on one occasion the sound of a coffin splitting
deep underground.

Children play on a rock where I once climbed,
perhaps the last stone from an old garden,
nothing remaining but this, a broken fountain,
one withered tree, its trunk scored by a bullet.
And on the path taking an evening stroll,
is Count Joseph Emanuel Canal de Malabaila,
his cloak bruising the heads of flowers,
while night pours sunset like the bloodied waters
that engulfed Marat, then rips out shadows
as a tailor pulls tacked sleeves.

What's this *'Jews not admitted.'* Well!

All that happens has happened before.
Lovers, beware of kisses that are not new-born,
each of us walks towards his own abyss.

By the pool is placed a goddess in white stone,
body curved like whipped cream. Fugitive
from an antique world, she covers her breasts,
leans to interrogate her quivering reflection
fringed by pink lilies, which brings us
by indirect route to the year 1829
and the young man who stood in the stalls
of the Stavovske Theatre to catch a glimpse
of the countess he adored, this poet
who lived in Michalska Street at the Red Cockerel,
his room without furniture, his writing table the floor.
The countess entered her box, sat in a velvet armchair,
lowered spiked lashes – carnivorous plant.
'Cover your eyes, you will drive me mad.'
Which she did.

As for the noble count, he deployed musicians
to play flutes in the shrubberies from which
such language breathed their music became love songs.
'Do you hear them? Will you honour me with this dance?'

Should the tip of one breast have spelt a message
in Morse code on my coat while we spun
it might have been chance, though I'd have given my life
for such a *billet doux* yet missed the boat
when she spread her skirts on the grass
laughing for someone else, and this way and that
went my life until one day she invited with a smile
because words seemed too bold, loitering for me
to catch up: *'I'll follow you as far as that place*
where sulphurous flowers cling the crater's edge.'
This was too far. A convulsion shook her
as if death had taken one arm. She scraped
her mouth across mine and bit hard.

So my love you escaped into snow and silence,
from the scent of jasmine that had filled our windows.
I met you too late. Now I give you *carte blanche*
to tear up my poems, burn letters. Just one request –
hold my head in your hands as you used to.
The count, countess, musicians, lovers have died.
The poet is dead and I search in vain
for the garden's last dead stone.

Never Again
Adapted from Ewald Osers' translation of Jaroslav Seifert

In Kralupy,
a hundred houses were flattened,
more than a thousand damaged
in air attacks.
I didn't count exactly how many,
picking my way through craters
that gaped horrifically.

Debris was carted off,
but although they dug fast,
it took three days to open up
the small house in Sverma Street
of the Hrncir family,
all of them dead ·
except the rooster
who crowed on a pile of rubble,
flapping his wings
to shake off dust.

In shock from what I'd seen,
the grief and pain on people's faces,
I spoke, first softly,
then I shouted into the silence,
loud so that war would hear –
'Never again war!'

The rooster,
descendant of one unloved
by the apostle Peter,
fixed me with basalt eye,
screeched raucously,
mocking my pointless raving.
Traitor!
He was after all a bird
and in league with planes.

Author's note: I am very grateful to Ewald Osers for the translations which
sparked off these versions.

Jaroslav Seifert (1901-1986). Winner of Nobel Prize for Literature in 1984. Ewald Osers has translated over 100 books of poetry/prose from Czech and German into English. Valerie Clarke won first
prize in the Blue Nose Poet of the Year competition 2000/2001 and has won prizes in other com-
petitions including Peterloo 2002. She has been published in various magazines and 'On the Buses'.
Her collection *Dance of Love and Death* was published in 2001 by the National Poetry Foundation.

Ron Sandford / Northern Lights

Uphellia galley figurehead/ Northern Lights above Shetland: Bluemull Sound; Burrafirth;
Mid Yell Voe; and Cullivoe Harbour/ Ming Sandford waving the Italian peace flag

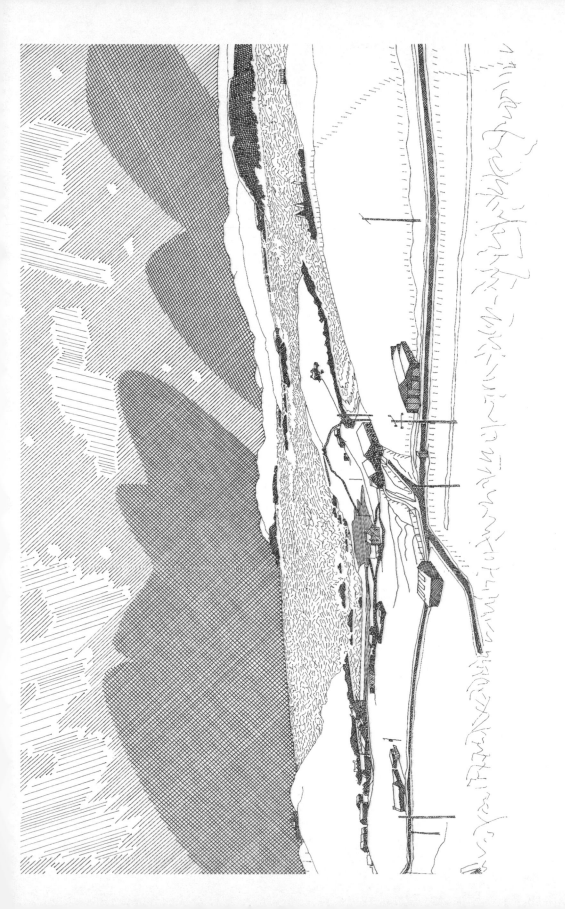

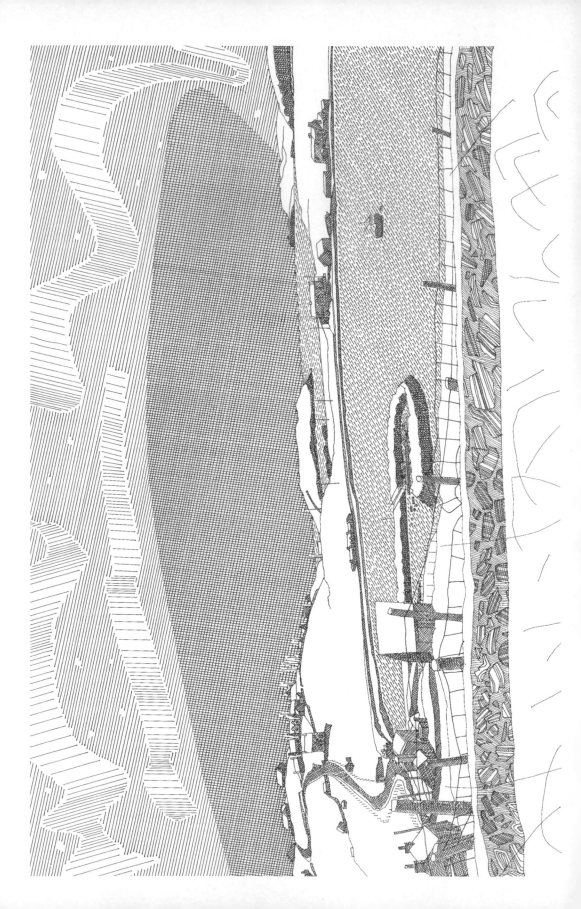

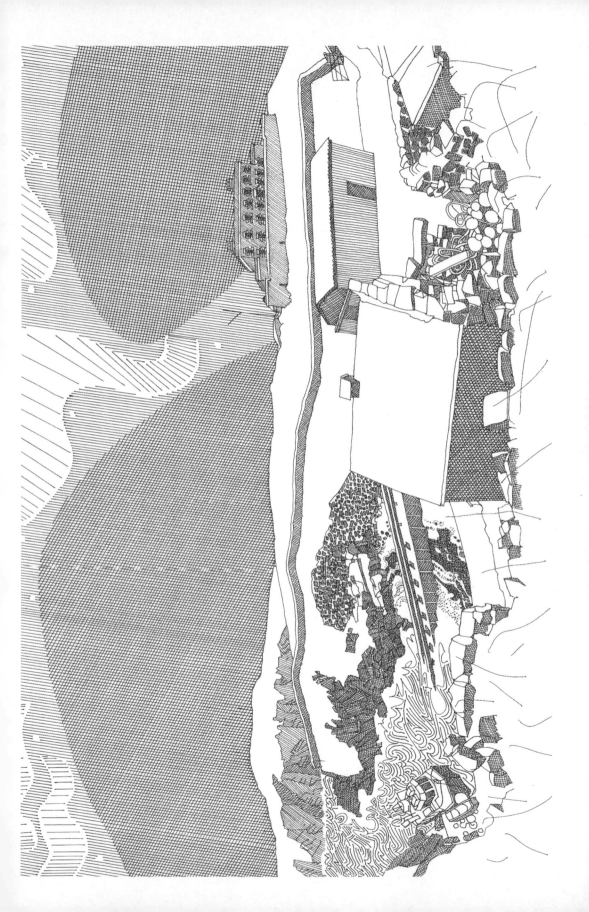

Valeria Melchioretto

The Unknown

From my mother I inherited a path paved with gallbladder stones,
wide as childbearing hips, twice the length of impatience.

From my father's side I inherited stories he told with his eyes.
Stories of death that no one mentioned, deep as afterthoughts.

He might have heard them like whispers from a war prisoner bed.
Mother would say thoughts were like boats, they need an anchor.

Nobody in our family could navigate an afterthought but it shook
our imagination like seasickness until we were green under our rosy cheeks.

In his sleep his eyelids flickered as if a factory was constructing nightmares
daylight didn't want to know about. From here I chose my path with care.

The Widow and the Window Cleaner

Her name was Rose but she had more in common with an
Arctic Poppy or Cotton Grass and was rooted in hard work.
She saved her words for long letters to her sister in Michigan.
Soapy Smith didn't bubble up her heart but he smiled like
Thanksgivings and made her golden potatoes sing in their skins.

He was overwhelmed, for he had never met such a solid woman
and her eyes reminded him of the windows on the large buildings
in Manhattan which he could clean for ever without getting tired.
The Northern Lights glowed above their wedding cake and
during their honeymoon the sun just rolled on below the horizon.

The Normal Head

Mother says that in the normal head
turqoise rivers of reason flow with the tide,
always in tune with the celestial pull.

She picks up her thimble, tears the thread,
searches for the needle with the biggest eye
in her skull shaped sewing kit.

She says sunlight is stored in memory hills,
bright people have glowing mountains.
The reason sources clear as spring water.

Imagination creeps under the skull like soil,
some fertile, some not. It is the colour of hungry irises.
Through their open mouths scent goes everywhere.

Steadily she stitches things best forgotten,
mends the moth damaged past, hems the future
and patches up silky suspicions torn under the skin.

She says normal brains have blue centres,
cool places, fun places, social stuff.
They unwind effortlessly as bobbins.

Deep in the kit I find black clouds. She won't explain.
She doesn't associate them with the normal head.
Those are the parts that hurt most.

Valeria Melchioretto was born in Switzerland to Italian parents. She has published work in magazines such as Poetry London, Poetry Wales, Salzburg Review and The Wolf. She currently lives in London.

Helena Nelson

An Erotic Poem for Mice

In absence, not presence,
the soft suggestion;
sleight of sense,
squirm of question.

Dust demurs
on the tender paw;
whisker stirs
a shadow, a spoor

of pink delight,
open and over.
Off in the night
the scurried lover.

Self-Portrait as the Song of Solomon

I am freckled, but comely,
　O ye daughters of Caledonia,
　　as the smooth side of a fresh trout
　as the stippled flesh of a barbecued salmon.
Look not upon me, because I am freckly,
　because my genes are celtic genes.
　　My mother's family were angry with me;
　because I went away to Scotland;
　　but mine own country have I not kept.
A motor mechanic is my well-beloved unto me;
　he shall lie all night in our double bedroom.
My beloved is unto me as a fragrance of diesel
　in the fuel tank of an Audi.
Behold, thou art fair, my love;
　behold, thou art fair in thy red boiler suit.
Behold, thou art fair, my beloved,
　yea, my treasure:
　　also our bed is king-sized.
The roof of our conservatory is glass
　and our garage non-existent.

'Dip me in chocolate and throw me to the lesbians.'

The T-shirt's directive
leaves much unanswered. For instance –
what kind of chocolate?
I think it would be couverture,
almost certainly Lindt.
Dark, not milk; bitter, not sweet. Still
some ambiguity –
who's the dippee? Garment? Wearer?
Wearer, I'd say, because
I am so utterly in love
with the mental picture
of smeary footprints, innocent
record of forced landing;
the victim excited but thrown,
scared of those slick quick tongues,
the brief invitation of jaws.

The Cure

I will say to the doctor –

Make me ill.
I've been well, too well,
for fifty years
and it's time, my time,
for the cool sheets
and the patient press
of quiet disease.
Let me be ill.
I will wear distress
like frost on velvet,
like dust on lace.

The doctor will say –

Health is your sickness.
Weal is your woe.
Go to the priest.
Go now. *Go.*

Helena Nelson's first full collection, *Starlight on Water*, was published by Rialto Press in 2003. She has still not recovered from the shock.

Carraroe in Saxony
Philip Mc Donagh
Dedalus Press £7.95

Philip McDonagh is a well-established and sophisticated traveller, a diplomat by profession and, we're told, currently Irish ambassador to India. His poems reflect his experiences, not so much, perhaps, in terms of international politics, but more in the personal sense of people met and places experienced during the course of his wanderings around the world. The names are scattered through the poems – Brussels, Geneva, Prague, Copenhagen, Rome, and so on. And sometimes going to a place can bring back memories of an earlier visit:

Nostalgia: the pain of going back
As I go back
led even by the camber of the streets
to find, among the spot-lit gilt facades,
that alcoved room
where we caught on together,
nothing again the same.

It's tidy poetry, quiet and easy in its rhythms and never pushing what it has to say in too forceful a way. The long title poem, autobiographical as the poet from the distance of Dresden recalls his dead mother and recreates her Irish world, never loses its elegiac pace nor its thoughtful cadence:

I pay up, leave the Elbterrasse,
stroll towards the monuments of town
imagining the forest in
an age of pilgrim, innocent
of dream-encasing promenades.

I've possibly given the impression that McDonagh ignores the world of power and politics altogether but that isn't the case. More than a few of the poems do refer to things like the Berlin Wall, the election of Ronald Reagan to President, and the friction between India and Pakistan. There are also historical references to the First World War and the British presence in India. As I said earlier, McDonagh is well-educated and knows how to blend such matters into the personal areas that define why and how his poems were written. And it's this mixture that makes them immensely readable as they chronicle his movements through the contemporary world and the manner in which his mind deals with history in both its personal and wider senses. **Jim Burns**

When They Come for You
Michael Swan
Frogmore Press £5.95

Michael Swan, we are told, "clings to the belief that it is possible to write good poetry that is neither difficult nor boring." It's an admirable sentiment and the only problem is that, reading it, you tend to wonder if the poetry will match up to it? In Swan's case it sometimes does, and when he's at his best he manages to produce poems that hold the interest of the reader, state their case clearly, and sustain a loose, rhythmic flow that, if not exactly exciting, at least doesn't hold up the action:

It was a very clever ghost.
Always somewhere else.
If she looked under the bed
it was in the drawer with her blouses;
when she went to the drawer
it slipped behind the curtain
trailing a smell of lavender.

What may be a problem with Swan's poems is that though they're not difficult or boring, they are sometimes a bit predictable. A poem called 'My neighbour' explores the old idea of the man of action versus the poet in his ivory tower. The neighbour can do all sorts of practical things and probably doesn't regret not being able to write a villanelle or trace an etymology. It's the poet who is envious and wants to knock a few nails in and sing 'Eskimo Nell' with the lads in the pub. But the poem doesn't tell us anything more than that and it's not enough.

But there are good poems in this collection. The title poem, for example, neatly deals with the idea of the moment when, in a sense, you're called to answer for your actions. And by leaving the situation open by not specifying exactly what it relates to, Swan lets the reader use it in his or her own way. It could be the moment you're carted off to the old people's home or prison or a variety of other places.

This isn't a bad book and Michael Swan does stay faithful to his theory of writing interesting poems in a direct way. It could be, though, that he needs to look for more original themes if he wants to convince us that what he has to say is of importance. **Jim Burns**

The Awakening: Poems Newly Found
Jack Clemo
Francis Boutle £7.95

I'm not sure how much Jack Clemo is read these days. I would guess that he still has currency in his native Cornwall but is there a wider readership for his work? And is it significant that this collection of previously unpublished poems comes from a small publisher? I'm not intending any criticism of Clemo when I ask these questions, and it's simply a matter of the fickleness of public taste and the fading reputations once writers die.

It could be, of course, that Clemo's religious beliefs, and the way in which they shaped his poetry, are not likely to appeal to many people in a country which is increasingly secular. Are the following lines the kind that contemporary audiences for poetry will want?

Lord, I can bring no sheaves,
No fruit to swell Thy store;
The year's last star-shaft leaves
Harsh glint on a barren floor.

Even the suggestion of religious doubt in that is hardly going to impress readers who may not ever have had any beliefs to doubt. But not all Clemo's poems were religious, and there was an erotic strain in some of his writing that the long and useful introduction to this book outlines. Clemo's questioning of his faith intertwined with a deep emotional attachment to a young girl which wasn't reciprocated. So, the poems often combine religion, eroticism, and a pantheistic relationship to the landscape of Cornwall. 'Midnight of the Flesh' has the religion and the eroticism:

To lie awake and stretch tired, yearning arms
where you, girl-phantom of my prison, glide,
And try and make love's wanton, secret charms
Turn shade to flesh for seed unsatisfied.

To call your name and woo the heedless air,
To speak, myself, what your ripe voice should say,
And burrow to the craven help of prayer,
Imploring Him who sneers in this delay.

As noted earlier, these are previously unpublished poems and they need to be read in conjunction with the introduction to see them in context and understand why they were written. It isn't necessary to share someone's beliefs to know how important they may be. **Jim Burns**

Nine Lessons From The Dark
Adam Thorpe
Cape £8.00

There is in Adam Thorpe's book a moving long poem about a friend, paralysed from the neck down and dying young, which more or less stopped me in my tracks when I read it. I'd been worrying about my own problems but the poem made me realise how insignificant they were compared to the young man's.

Now, I appreciate that this isn't the way some literary types will expect a reviewer to respond to a poem, though I sometimes wonder what poems are for if not to stop us in our tracks and make us think. But to forestall criticism of my response I will add that Thorpe's poem succeeds because of the way it is written and the skill with which he handles language and technique. A lesser work, not given the care Thorpe has evidently applied, would most likely allow the reader to react sympathetically to the young man's plight but without any great emotional involvement. What comes to mind is Ezra Pound's dictum, 'Don't tell me how you feel, make me feel it,' and it's Thorpe's achievement to make us all the time focus on the patient and not the visitor, though the pain the visitor feels comes through in what is described. I've deliberately not used any extracts from the poem because it needs to be read as a whole for its subtlety and depth of emotion to be fully appreciated.

'Nerve', the poem I've referred to, would alone be worth the price of the book, but there are others which are equally good in their own way. They have lines in them that stay in the mind, like those about an old lady, alone in London, which is described as "a prison/ of trip-wire pavements and dexterous shoves/ and the eternal flight of stairs to your nutshell room." And there's a poem which starts off with comments about the poet's father and becomes an observation on the limbo-like nature of airports:

My father worked in them for thirty years,

hassled by fog days, a prisoner of wings
and hijacks, fake bomb-calls, his singing in
                                    the ears
from standing in the shrieking reach of jets;
                                and thinks
flying has lost its elan, these days –
more like catching a bus, he says.

I want to keep on quoting from the poems –
"Lucy, I'm beat. It's sixteen hours a day and I'm
getting old," an old man says of his decision to
sell his farm – but it's perhaps better to just
recommend *Nine Lessons From The Dark* and so
let readers enjoy its pleasures for themselves.
Jim Burns

Manhattan Sonnets
Lynne Hjelmgaard
Redbeck Press £6.75

There is a style of writing that piles up images
and ideas in a way that makes it seem as if a
series of notes for a longer, more-detailed work
are being assembled. But the point is that the
notes, if we can call them that for convenience,
are the finished work. Take the following lines
from Lynne Hjelmgaards's book, for example:

With cool dude on lower East Side
First date in the Park, hold cigarette
Don't know how to, Joe demonstrates
In Italian, want to be cooler, me
At his house off Delancey and Broom
I'm shy in knee socks, unaware
Sofa bed folds out, takes the room
Me later, body tender in Square
One night sick with fever, but I call
His mother, Sorry Joe ain't here
Take bus downtown to no avail
Not words or note, just bruising air
I can't give in, go back, move forward
A child put off, who won't be spurned

There is a story there, and in fact it would
probably make a good short story, or even the
beginning of something longer, but we're only
given what we see and nothing more. Is it enough
or is the poet cheating us by refusing to develop
ideas or build on her memories? I'm not sure,
and I found myself also faced with the difficulties
inherent in reading at length what is a staccato
assemblage of words. There is a logical flow to
the writing, in the sense of it describing the

writer's experiences, but not all the short
sections sustain the same interest. Some seem
fairly inconsequential, especially in the second
part of the book, and others are too private for
meaningful communication. But there are a few
which come alive:

The Buddha Tree is too short
next to Blaise Cendrars' poems
I go through my books like neighbourhoods
and rest in the leafy corners of their bindings
The sensation of having them near me
their smell

I found this book quite fascinating without
thinking it successful in any overall way. As I've
indicated, its effect varies according to the
quality of the individual short sections, and it
may be that the best way to read it is quickly and
in tune with its nervous narration of growing up
in America in the 1960's and later living in Paris.
It can communicate the rhythms of a certain
lifestyle quite successfully if you can match its
mood. **Jim Burns**

In Praise of Men and Other People
Ann Sansom
Bloodaxe £7.95

Is there such a thing as 'Northern Poetry', by
which I suppose is meant poetry that not only
makes references to Northern places, or the
supposed characteristics of Northern people, but
also somehow captures the rhythms and
underlying feeling of life in the North? I've never
been convinced that there is, leaving aside
dialect poets and they often seem to be wishfully
thinking of an imagined region rather than a real
one. With shopping centres and supermarkets
and airports just down the road that can spirit
you to foreign climes, not to mention television
and the levelling out of tastes and interests, it's
hard to hang on to an identity related to a
specific area.

And yet there are poets who manage it and
Ann Sansom is among them. Her poems – 'an
authentic Northern mix of realism and
imagination', as one critic describes them – have
a kind of matter-of-factness mixed with humour
and sympathy that does truly suggest the mood
and atmosphere of certain places. I couldn't see
the following lines being descriptive of anywhere
outside the North, though their wider meaning

applies everywhere:

The river comes through the city,
clear black even in summer but tonight,
late January, it's cracked at the weir
on burst red stars, bus windows. You could die
of cold, this lead frost could weight
your lungs, piles stones in your pockets.

It's authentic and the tone and directness (almost bluntness) of the statements add to the reality of the picture. Reading those lines I can feel the frost and see the dark buildings against the winter sky. It may be a personal fancy, but I am reminded of Atkinson's Grimshaw's wonderful Victorian paintings of Northern cities at night.

I don't want to suggest that the poems are in any way limited by being identified with a region. Much of the best poetry in any age starts off with the local and then moves beyond it to the wider application of what is seen and experienced. Ann Sansom does that widening with skill and imagination. The reader never feels excluded from the world she describes because the poems communicate what it is like to see and understand what the poet experiences. This is a book with a great deal of writing that rings true and rarely fails to match up to what is expected of it. **Jim Burns**

Serious Angel
Jan Twardowski, trans. Sarah Lawson & Malgorzata Koraszewska
Dedalus: Waxwing Series No. 3, £7.95

Twardowski (b.1915) has been publishing prolifically since 1959 and is the best-loved poet in Poland.

A retired priest, he writes: "I didn't come to convert you." The poems can be as austere as R.S. Thomas: to someone dying who "To the last moment never stopped talking... I explained that awaiting him/ is just one word which is silence". But they can be funnier:

The door trembled: 'Who's there?'
'Death.'
He came in, tiny
Little with a scythe like a matchstick,
Astonishment. Eyes out on stalks.
And he:
'I came for the canary.'

He prefers the small voice: "Lord Jesus I think You don't like being tortured with organs in churches/ You've had enough of Bach's music –/ maybe you'd like to hear/ how a Hebrew letter creaks in the Bible on its black legs..." He hopes that even theologians can be saved – "so they'll not eat up all the candles and sit in darkness..." He loves creatures: if God hadn't hidden himself "who would dare to notice an ant/ a beautiful wicked wasp bustling around..." "Every single tree is a non-believer... a dog very seldom goes to church." He likes the sparrow that "astonished by Grace/ tumbled/ into the holy water".

I tramp through the world like a heavy
                                    elephant
so big that I understand nothing
I think how to kneel
and not have my nose in the air.

This is a priest who has no answers, only prophetic questions. Nevertheless he hands out paradox on the mysteries: the Creator "created you so imperfect/ that you're good". Perhaps you don't need to be 'religious' yourself to feel the poems. **Herbert Lomas**

The Butcher's Hands
Catherine Smith
Smith/Doorstep Books £6.95

A lot of these poems are about when things are over but not forgotten. Uncle Aubrey, dying, "remembers dead cousins drunk at Christmas". A woman is gathering up the detritus of a life, including her son's plastic wristband worn at birth, and remembering the colour of her milk. An old wife outside her husband's bedroom remembers jitterbugging with the GI who took her virginity in her mother's front room. Another woman collects keepsakes to reconstruct the man on her bed at home, an alabaster egg for his heart, a sweaty sock for his prick. A couple meet their younger honeymooning selves at Zennor: "We could be planning an argument or a long kiss."

There are weirdos. A Grannie fantasises she has a boy baby in the airing cupboard upstairs and is baking for him: "He hardly ever cries." A man has a fetish for highly pregnant women, feels them in the tube or on lifts, pays one woman to let him lick her hump of a belly with the child kicking inside. A woman who has never done a single thing wrong or been tempted has her roses dead-headed by an alien. A manager of a freak show bills a bearded woman as "the ugliest woman in the world" and marries her to enjoy her. The hangman is a craftsman, studying the mathematics of drops: "I whisper to him he's in good hands." A woman has found a male plastic doll to love.

Death is not the end: a suicide resents both her husband's mourning and his remarriage. A woman fears her cremated husband might resurrect: "...or worse still, you'll slouch by my trolley/ at the cold meats counter, whisky-foul/ and lewd, chewing pastrami..." There are also bad dreams, sado-masochistic fantasies, a feral child who may never become human.

These stories and characters are well-written, well-observed and cheerful with it. There's a very evocative poem about fellatio comparing it to fresh, not dried, pasta *alle vongole* or *al funghi*. The point of all this cool look at tastelessness is evidently to illustrate how we're not as normal and respectable as we'd like to pretend. We're a weird lot, awake or asleep, but no worse for that. **Herbert Lomas**

Point / Erasing

Jean Portante, trans. Anne-Marie Glasheen
Dedalus: Poetry Europe Series 18 £7.95

The word 'point' here has its French meaning of 'not any', and there's play on other connotations. Does 'Point de Départ' mean 'Point of Departure' or 'No Departure' – pure antitheses? In love, for instance, this ambiguity points to the woman's ambivalence: "there is in your last glance unfinished business".

Many of the poems enact such an uncertain relationship. The door's bolted – not against the woman but against "the ghost of a stag":

He is from now on the sentry between
you and me and circumscribes our space
by urinating on the pavement

The book has a remarkable coherence, as though one strong driving emotion were behind every poem, with the stag as a running image. The mild surrealism makes its points, with feeling, as if it were the only natural way to speak. It allows a very concrete notation for the pain of rejection or, perhaps worse, semi-rejection.

This motorway which inside me tarmacs
the desire to stay opens like a zip
fastener the wound which yesterday evening
I brought
home.

"... we remain/ silent like that time in the kitchen when/ my mother was pouring ladles of silence/ into our plates"; "... is this how the day begins/ eyes blindfolded like a condemned man/ before the firing squad..."; "If there is anything that/ has neither a door nor/ a window it must be/ pain..."; "An enormous fly larger/ than a/ memory settles/ on my head/ when I look at you..."

One of the attractions of reading foreign verse is that the poets are not afraid of feeling. The heart on the sleeve can be very stylish. The grief seems all the more genuine for the elegant tropes and quiet-spoken hyperboles – which remind us that there are quite different ways of writing than ours.

Besides these faithful translations we have the French of this leading Luxembourg poet, who has published some twenty books – collections of poetry, short stories, plays, screenplays and novels. **Herbert Lomas**

Forced March

Miklós Radnóti, trans. George Gömöri & Clive Wilmer
Enitharmon £8.95

Radnóti was shot by the Nazis in 1944 at the age of thirty-five. His body was identified a year later from the poems in his pocket, which he'd been writing almost to the end in his labour camp. What's astonishing is that he seems to have long had prescience of the manner of his death, even before the war. "And as for you, young man, what mode of death awaits you?" He thought that fascism kills poets merely for being poets, because they're witnesses to the truth.

This selection is from his last three books, where horror is translated into formal beauty, influenced by French and German poetry, classical hexameters and the Bible. The result is, paradoxically, a kind of simplicity, as in this poem of 1938:

When I stepped out through the gate it was
just ten o'clock,

A baker sped by on gleaming wheels, a song
on his lips,
A plane droning high overhead and the sun
up, it was ten,
And my dead sister came into my mind and
with that they were all
Flying above me – those whom I love and
those who are not alive –
Darkly across the sky a host of the silent dead.
Then, a jolt, and a shadow crumpled against
the wall.
Silence. The morning came to a halt on the
stroke of ten;
Hovering over the street, peace – and a certain
horror.

Wondering "at being alive tonight", the poet consoles himself by singing about his fate, both foreseen and experienced. "Keep walking, you, the death-condemned…", "A dark autumnal mist drips on the grave…", "There on the bush wet chaos breeds…", "People are murdered all the time,/ Somewhere…", "I am a poet and unnecessary… Who knows that, in the end, he will be killed/ Because he would not kill."

It's vocation and resignation raised to a kind of weird joy, with the "terrible angel" not screaming but making a sound "slight as a grasshopper's": "I never did have anything and never shall do now./ …The world will be rebuilt and where the new walls start/ My song, which is now banned, will be heard again…" (April 1944).

Hungarians regard Radnóti as one of the most important twentieth-century European poets. A synthesis of Judaeo-Christian socialism, he became increasingly preoccupied with body-soul relationships, the ways of the soul after death and the establishment of a socialist kingdom of God, via a possibly terminal condition of civilisation.

Those who know say this is the best translation, and I can believe it. **Herbert Lomas**

Orient Express Vols. 1 & 2, 226 pp
ed. Fiona Sampson
Wythgreen House, Coleshill, SN6 7PS
£5·00 + pp

Named after the glamorous wagon-lit railway – Paris, Vienna, Budapest, Bucharest, Istanbul – with connections to every European capital en route, this English-language magazine attempts to ferry readers across the evolving literature of Europe. It's luxury-class and good reading.

There are journal entries from the famous Estonian Jaan Kaplinski, generous selections from three Romanian women poets, poems by Cevat Çapan, whose persona says "He's never written a word/ that wasn't written for a beautiful girl", stories by – well, so many others whose alien names conceal so much humanity. Worth a trip, and much cheaper than any airfare.
Herbert Lomas

www.ambitmagazine.co.uk

Poems / Fiction / Art / Reviews

James Russell

Cheers!

The basic physics of light on Naomi's pillow
The peach down of neck-nape, the awakening
To the brute fact of the day: she has outnumbered
Herself. Poured out now into shot-glass measures
Ranged, as 'twere, along her side-board they supervened
Upon the moral and the murmur of her stroll through sorrow.

But this day of sun could not hold her long in the grip of sorrow,
When fields shone about her cottage, once supervened
On by a civil war battle where – epiphanous awakening –
An army triumphed though ragged and outnumbered.
Broken heads shared these fields as their pillow.
The pillow beside hers was empty. What measures

Will she now be taking? Naomi had no cache of measures.
But she had her man Jack, a gardener-visitor to her pillow
Of Cavalier hair and Roundhead gait whose love for her supervened
On stalled actions, upon his wait for her clarion call from sorrow –
(Every ten minutes a sucked cigarette by his fingers outnumbered.)
Then like a speaker's tapped glass she chimed various awakening.

'I cannot collect myself,' he (or they) murmured awakening.
(Think The Beverely Sisters in *en face* mirrors.) Still point outnumbered
His fluids spent like libido across old leather flaskettes – measures
Of Jackhood only fit for a saddlebag on a shining-field ride to her pillow
Here were distributed agents of soaring and sorrow
Below them a charcoal and *crème fraiche* grey mixture – the supervened.

On an Old West map a burning-match movie line supervened
On his bike ride bang to her cottage. His stooping frame measures
Her floor to her ceiling. Speech is a chorus of shouting down sorrow
Of gardening a pair of pink buds to awakening.
He kneels to her couch-bound, her legs tucked like a puppet's, her pillow
Clutched hard to her belly, minority rule in her outnumbered

Mind. 'Have you breakfasted Jack? My fridge is outnumbered
By finger foods in cool abundance. Kiss me to dignify sorrow.
We are free refugees, let light be our pillow.'
His big knees cracked as he stood, iconoclast glory supervened

On his stride, as 'twere to her sideboard. Drinking the first of her measures
Said 'Cheers!', threw his saddlebag cache to his girl. Their awakening

To thirst outnumbered the null class of sorrow,
Stuffed as a pillow with the now-supervened –
On, each had the other's measures – each to the other awakening.

Ghost Characters

They neither show nor speak up,
Are tongue-tied in a compound of reported speech
Behind the act/inhibit razor wire
Gleaming in the public sun –
The wire life-long and quick as a water snake.

Damp and empty as a just-washed cup
They stand and wait, they interface, each
Is the master of a flip-side role. Desire:
Fulfilled by bringing out a fresh print-run
Of their shadow-land impedimenta. Their sake

Is the other's sake. Wardrobe-bound incubi who sup
The dust and moth-breath of the dark, who leech
Nothing from dreams, these ghost characters cannot fire
Up their souls, but are millions to your one.
To fight them off be latinate, conceptual, opaque.

In a coffee hour one of Cornish's ghost characters spoke up.
As simple as a just-peeled lychee was its speech
In a voice the colour of calamine lotion. 'Wire
Yourselves to us', it said. 'Bask in the shadow sun.
Free us (your poison) like a snake.'

From that day on nothing mattered, all games were up
The department had nothing at all to teach;
Its stock of authority had expired.
There was nothing in anything for anyone.
Look for a table for your teacup in an earthquake?

The Academic Secretary and his mother now dress up
As cops and see what they can do. The sweet, peach-
Coloured ribbon that once was the act/inhibit razor wire
Lies on a muddy path trodden on by everyone.
Logically impossible – yes really – to make a mistake.

Things' happy knack of never looking down or up
Was celebrated campus-wide in seminars in which the cup
Was raised above the knitted brow. For these chaps to sup

And spout was for the overhead projectors to be granted speech.
So many sentences had shone through them, each
Immaculate and buzzing buzzing in dimmed rooms, leech

Though they might a sense of being made outside the wire
It was better in this melted world to have a ghost desire
Woven from all the not-done and the not-I, stepping from a fire

Far flung from the public sun,
Loving the weather of the giant's thumb, loving to run
From the explicit, eliding themselves with anyone.

To live with your shed skin as an ancient snake,
For the wordless god and for goodness sake
Avoid the latinate, conceptual, opaque.

James Russell is a reader in psychology at Cambridge. His poems have previously appeared in PN
Review, Thumbscrew, and Blackwater (Eire). His collection *The Sixty-Four Seasons* is to appear this
Spring from Oleander.

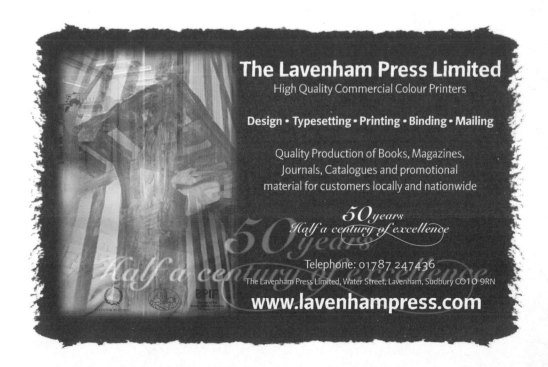

Anthony Howell

How Sad Everything Is

Fuelled by Coca-Cola Lite,
This machine cannot have babies.
It is a work of Platonic abstraction
Subject to scrupulous maintenance
For reasons which are over-determined.

Jennifer Lopez, I love Jennifer Lopez!
She's got a big bum,
And wants an even bigger one.

Half the world hasn't got enough.
The other half toys with its dinner.
What about the children in Africa?
At least they can have children:
Got their tubes working – unlike ours.

Jennifer Lopez, I love Jennifer Lopez!

The supplement was showing off atrocities:
People got impaled in Cambodia.
How sad everything is, he said.
Some of their eyes are still moving.
People get impaled almost anywhere.

Said Jennifer...

Me, I got impaled, up in Cambridge.
Don't see the point now in food.
Want to wear death-camp pyjamas,
Want to have legs like a bird.
Why do what my doctor says?

Jennifer Lopez!

Anthony Howell's new book of poems *Dancers in Daylight* has just been published by Anvil.
His new performance Tango Art was recently performed at the Irish Centre, London.

Tricia Cherin

Last Fucks

The early ones are momentous
lovely in their way of course
but fraught with what the cliché
calls performance anxiety

what is really just coming to terms
with the crux of human experience
nuance, allusion, reference
here they are plain as day

what it means to be transcendent and
feral, god and animal all at once
to know finally
what the fuss is all about

I'm starting to rehearse now
the last time
the doing it after which
it will all be finally done

the last great fuck
is perhaps more poignant
than the first dear ones
the dark lust so clear now

no longer touch resents
its burden, always
carrying more than itself
many histories in every caress

even yearning is more so
because of accumulations and contexts
if ever there will be a knowing
it must be now

after all the tryouts
the dearest coupling happens
tenderness and passion finally poised
joy wisely accommodating

touch will never be more sure
or bodies more durable
they are learned now
and weighted with living and doing

in the final familiar mysteries
there is somber abandon
such good practice
for the near oblivion

Fuss

It's 4:30 in the morning
and I can't wait to
get up from bed
to give the universe

a poke with a stick
and a strike
on thin stretched skin
there at the meridian

it's not enough just now
to go through the motions
fulfill the rigmarole
I want attitude on the agenda

I want the world today
to poke back
to play and tease
delight in me

to be hearty, staunch and hale
and if it's weary or had it
(I can be trying)
well, tough shit

go at it, dear humors
I'm ready for the riling
a physics of consequence
sweet commotion

Sea Owls

All over the place
here at the edge of the continent
are wooden owls on roofs and rails
wise sentries peering over ocean

at first they seem out of place
seahorses would be more thematic
copper whales more fitting
but these are scarecrows

that keep the gulls from shitting
on elegant patios
there is more stock in a place
where the unsuited is embraced

the sea needs these forest totems
carved birds
foretelling inland,
dense and timbered center

Winter Beach

Kelp as thick around
as a giant's femur
against a golden gourd
like a knuckle
and sea grass
newly wrenched

the fog horn moans
soprano on bass clef
historied grief

a pelican flies
against the crescent moon
on the threshold of
more than itself

just for this moment

Tricia Cherin teaches the graduate seminar in Texts and Language at California State University Dominguez Hills. She has over 80 publications including two chapbooks, *Familiarities* (with Gerald Locklin) and *Park Quest*. She lives in Long Beach, California just across from the Queen Mary.

Gwen MacKeith.
'Se una notte d'inverno (Oct 3'03)
un viaggiatore'